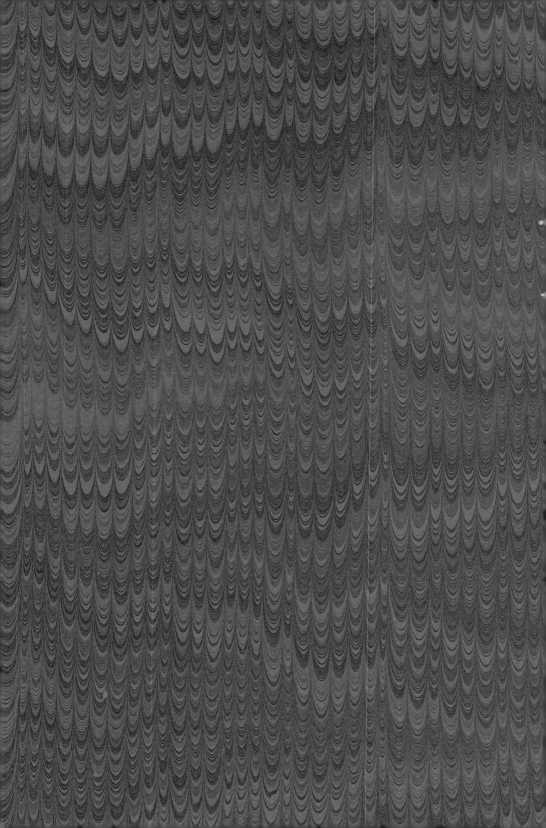

A Son
and his
Adoptive Father

THE MARQUIS DE LAFAYETTE AND GEORGE WASHINGTON

By
Christine H. Messing
John B. Rudder
Diane Windham Shaw

Foreword by
His Excellency Jean-David Levitte
Ambassador of France to the United States

A Companion to a Traveling Exhibition
organized by
The Mount Vernon Ladies' Association

This exhibition was created to inaugurate the
F. M. Kirby Foundation Gallery
at the
Donald W. Reynolds Museum and Education Center
at George Washington's Mount Vernon

Principal support was provided by

The F. M. Kirby Foundation

The Florence Gould Foundation

The Founders, Washington Committee
for Historic Mount Vernon

The Embassy of France

and other generous benefactors

Exhibition Design by

Charles Mack Design and

Quenroe Associates

Published by

The Mount Vernon Ladies' Association

2006

Table of Contents

Exhibition Itinerary

The F. M. Kirby Foundation Gallery in the
Donald W. Reynolds Museum and Education Center
at Mount Vernon
October 27, 2006 through August 5, 2007

Lafayette College Art Gallery
Williams Center for the Arts
August 27 through October 28, 2007

The New-York Historical Society
November 13, 2007 through March 9, 2008

Entries in the publication are followed by a key that
indicates where individual pieces can be seen:
MVLA: Mount Vernon
LC: Lafayette College
N-YHS: New-York Historical Society

At left, Life mask of Lafayette by Jean-Antoine Houdon, plaster, July 1785, side view. Gift of Arthur H. Dean, Class of 1919, and Mary Marden Dean. Courtesy of the Herbert F. Johnson Museum of Art, Cornell University. Above, Washington & Lafayette at the Battle of Brandywine by John Vanderlyn, oil on canvas, ca.1825. From the collection of the Gilcrease Museum, Tulsa, Oklahoma.

Drawn by A. Chappel.   Engraved by J. De Mare.

Lafayette

From an authentic Portrait in the possession of the Publishers.

Martin, Johnson & Co. Publishers, N.Y.

Preface

In 2007, both France and the United States will commemorate the 250th anniversary of the birth of Gilbert du Motier, Marquis de Lafayette, who played a critical role in winning the American colonies' independence from Great Britain.

At the remarkable age of nineteen, Lafayette sailed from France and volunteered to fight—quite literally, in battle—for the struggling American cause. He soon gained the trust, admiration, and affection of General George Washington. Lafayette also deftly employed his important connections in French society and the art of persuasion to secure much-needed supplies, troops, and substantial financial aid for America's Continental Army, and he made the case for France to enter the war. It proved to be the turning point, as French and American forces joined together at Yorktown for the decisive military engagement of the war. The victorious soldiers lined up (French on one side of the road and Americans on the other) as the defeated British marched between them. Americans have not forgotten the contributions of Rochambeau, d'Estaing, and de Grasse, but it is Lafayette who won their hearts, perhaps because of his "father-son" relationship with Washington. The people of the United States warmly embraced him during his lifetime and mourned him deeply at his death. It was at his grave in Paris during World War I—when the United States came to the aid of France in our hour of need— that an American officer proclaimed "Lafayette, we are here!" to acknowledge the profound debt felt for Lafayette's pivotal contributions. Even today, if you visit Lafayette's grave, you will see an American flag standing proud and strong.

I applaud Mount Vernon, Washington's home, and Lafayette College for working together to bring this splendid exhibition honoring Washington and Lafayette to fruition. There is no more telling manifestation of the two men's deep bond than the main key to the Bastille, the fortress prison whose destruction Lafayette ordered at the beginning of the French Revolution. Lafayette sent the key to his hero, the first President of the United States, along with a letter, that read in part: "It is a tribute Which I owe as A Son to My

At left, Lafayette at Yorktown, J. de Mare, after Alonzo Chappel, engraving, 1857. David Bishop Skillman Library, Lafayette College.

Adoptive father, as an aid de Camp to My General, as a Missionary of liberty to its patriarch." Washington cherished this key and brought it to Mount Vernon when retiring from the presidency, placing it in the heart of his home where every guest would see it. This exhibition marks only the third time that this key has left Mount Vernon in more than two hundred years. (I am happy to say that the first occasion was the bicentennial of the French Revolution when the key was hand-carried from Washington's estate to France.) It will be seen and appreciated by more than a million people as it travels with this exhibition.

So let us commemorate two heroic leaders who, despite differences in age and nationality, were united in their quest for liberty. Since the Treaty of Alliance cemented the bond between France and America, it has lasted through good times and bad. May we continue to stand together as we did at Yorktown and salute the solid and enduring friendship between our two countries. *Vive Washington! Vive Lafayette!*

Jean-David Levitte
Ambassador of France to the United States

Acknowledgments

This exhibition inaugurates Mount Vernon's new changing exhibitions gallery—The F. M. Kirby Foundation Gallery in the Donald W. Reynolds Museum and Education Center. Although we have organized several temporary exhibitions over the past few years and traveled them to museums across the country, we have never had the opportunity, until now, to create a major show on the estate for our nearly one million annual visitors.

We have enjoyed a happy collaboration with Lafayette College in Easton, Pennsylvania, founded in 1826 in honor of the Marquis de Lafayette. The college has a rich collection of material related to Lafayette, as well as a number of artifacts related to George Washington. The idea for the exhibition first arose with Stephen Hartwell and Fred Benson, Lafayette College alumni who long have been involved with the Mount Vernon Ladies' Association through their leadership of The Life Guard Society and the Mount Vernon Advisory Committee, respectively. The concept was warmly—and almost immediately—embraced by the college staff. We are particularly indebted to Diane Windham Shaw, Michiko Okaya, and Eric Luhrs who cheerfully assisted in countless ways. Diane probably knows more about Lafayette artifacts than anyone in America—she may even rival her colleagues in France—and her insightful essay on the relationship between Washington and Lafayette is the driving force of this publication.

When looking for the perfect venue in New York City, we recalled how much we enjoyed working with the New-York Historical Society when we introduced our "Treasures from Mount Vernon" exhibition in late 1998. Now that the Society has become the headquarters for the Gilder Lehrman Institute of American History collection, it has become an even more attractive partner. It has been a pleasure and privilege to work with the Society's president, Louise Mirrer, as well as Linda Ferber, Roy Eddey, Margaret Hofer, and Kathleen Hulser.

Two brothers, Jeff and Dillard Kirby, have been involved with our new museum, the changing exhibition gallery, and this particular show for the last three years. Their personal interest—as well as the incredibly generous support of the F. M. Kirby Foundation—has been far greater than that of a typical foundation. It has given us the confidence and encouragement to "think big" from the start. They have both visited Mount Vernon to check on our progress, and their admiration of Lafayette, the college, as well as Lafayette, the man, has no bounds.

Tom Pulling, a very active member of the Advisory Committee, and our Vice Regent for New York, Beatrice Guthrie, encouraged us to contact the Florence Gould Foundation, which has supported so many worthy projects that celebrate the relationship between France and America. The Foundation's generous gift enabled us to enhance the exhibition in terms of both the quantity and quality of the artifacts.

His Excellency Jean-David Levitte, Ambassador of France to the United States, was so gracious and kind to host in his exquisite home a benefit reception and historical reenactment, co-sponsored by The Founders, Washington Committee for Historic Mount Vernon. Having worked side by side with the remarkable women who make up The Founders Committee for some twenty-three years, I can testify to the fact that the only kind of event they know how to organize is a successful and festive one.

Fortunately, we have a number of Francophiles among our loyal Mount Vernon supporters, who came forth with special gifts, usually above-and-beyond their annual giving, to demonstrate their enthusiasm for this show. Leading the way were Dr. and Mrs. Bruce Ammerman, Mrs. Josephine F. Ammerman, Dr. and Mrs. William M. Busey, The Honorable Mary K. Bush, Mr. and Mrs. Donald Chamberlin, Jr., Mrs. Kevin P. Charles, Mr. and Mrs. Stan Chincheck, Mr. and Mrs. Stephen D. Clouse, Mr. and Mrs. Louis R. Cohen, Mrs. Elsie Moreland Corro, Mr. and Mrs. Theodore F. Craver, Capt. James D. Huck and Ms. Jeanne M. Defliese, Mr. and Mrs. Bruce W. Eberle, Mr. and Mrs. John W. Fisher, Mr. and Mrs. Stanley N. Gaines, Mr. and Mrs. Stewart Gammill III, Mr. John V. Gibson, Dr. and Mrs. Randolph H. Guthrie, Mr. and Mrs. Bradley Hale, Mr. and Mrs. David E. Holt, Jr., Mr. Thomas S. Kenan III, Mr. and Mrs. Knight A. Kiplinger, Mr. and Mrs. Gerhardt P. Kraske, Ms. Sherri P. Lee, Mr. Hunter Lewis and Ms. Elizabeth Sidamon-Eristoff, Mr. and Mrs. Christopher M. Little, Mrs. William G. Marr, Mr. and Mrs. James C. Meade, Mrs. Mary B. O'Connor, Mr. and Mrs. James D. Penny, Mrs. Brian Pohanka, Mr. and Mrs. John J. Pohanka, Mr. and Mrs. James E. Porter, Mr. Frederick H. Prince, Mr. and Mrs. Lawrence J. Ramer, Mr. and Mrs. Arthur G. Randol III, Mr. and Mrs. Sean Regan, Ms. Melody Sawyer Richardson, Mr. and Mrs.

Everette C. Sherrill, Mr. and Mrs. Albert H. Small, Mr. and Mrs. T. Eugene Smith, Mr. Ben S. Stefanski II, Mr. and Mrs. Richard J. J. Sullivan, Jr., Mr. and Mrs. P. Coleman Townsend, Jr., Mr. Harlow G. Unger, Col. and Mrs. Marvin A. Westphal, Ms. Karen Buchwald Wright, and Mr. Jeffrey Zell.

As always, Mount Vernon's staff came through with flying colors in taking care of all the details—both large and small—to make the exhibition a success. Linda Ayres, Director of Collections, personally took charge of this special effort, despite the extraordinary demands resulting from the opening of our new museum. Robert H. Smith Senior Curator Carol Borchert Cadou offered suggestions along the way, Assistant Curator Christine H. Messing and Special Projects Manager John B. Rudder researched and selected objects and contributed catalog entries and label copy, and Research Specialist Mary V. Thompson conducted invaluable research, compiled the timeline, and bibliography. I also want to recognize the contributions of Collections Manager Mary Margaret Carr, Exhibitions Registrar Elizabeth Sumner, Librarian Barbara McMillan, Administrative Specialist Dawn Bonner, Conservator Katherine Ridgway, and former conservation staff members Flavia Perugini and Simona Cristanetti. Space prevents us from listing individually the numerous staff members who helped in so many different ways.

Our talented designers—Charles Mack and Heather Ersts of Charles Mack Design, and Elroy Quenroe of Quenroe Associates—worked alongside our staff every step of the way. They gave freely of their considerable talent, good taste, and extensive experience with some of the most accomplished museums in the country. I also want to thank the team at ELY, Inc., who augmented our Mount Vernon staff during the installation process.

In addition, we would like to thank the many talented people who cooperated on so many levels, over a period of more than two years, to make this exhibition possible: Emily Schulz, Ellen Clark, and Rebecca Cooper (The Society of the Cincinnati, Anderson House); Jeffrey Ray (Atwater Kent Museum of Philadelphia); Nancy Davis and Louise Brownell (Maryland Historical Society); Jessica Neuwirth (Old Sturbridge Village); Peter Dun Grover, Patricia A. Hobbs, and Angelika Kuettner (Washington and Lee University); Jacquelyn Serwer and Sarah Cash (Corcoran Gallery of Art); Johanna Brown and Abigail S. Linville (Museum of Early Southern Decorative Arts); Dr. Scott Edwards, Jeremiah Trimble, and Alison Pirie (Ornithology

Department, Museum of Comparative Zoology, Harvard University); Matthew Conway and Elaine D. Engst (Cornell University); Dr. Martin West (Fort Ligonier); Dr. Charles Pierce, Jr. (Morgan Library & Museum); Georges Renand and Isabelle-Sophie Grivet (Fondation Josée et René de Chambrun); James G. Basker, Sandra M. Trenholm, Ana Ramirez Luhrs, and Jody Cary (Gilder Lehrman Institute of American History); Gerard W. Gawalt, Edward Redmond, and Sara W. Duke (Library of Congress); Wendy Wick Reaves, Anne Collins Goodyear, and Amy Baskette (National Portrait Gallery); Philander D. Chase (*The Papers of George Washington*); Leslie L. Buhler, Wendy Kail, and Melinda L. Huff (Tudor Place Foundation, Inc.); Karin Wittenborg and Christian Y. Dupont (University of Virginia); Anne Wagner and Grace Eleazer (Winterthur Museum); Dr. Jean Lee (University of Wisconsin-Madison); Gail Serfaty and Lynn Turner (Diplomatic Reception Rooms, U.S. Department of State); Linda Thrift (CEROS, Smithsonian Institution); Natalie F. Larson (Historic Textile Reproductions); Bill Martin, Suzanne Savery, and Jackie Mullins (The Valentine Richmond History Center); and Anne Bentley (Massachusetts Historical Society).

It is clear that this exhibition reflects the hard work and generosity of many people. The idea of celebrating the relationship between George Washington and the Marquis de Lafayette has definitely struck a chord, and we are grateful beyond what words can adequately express.

As we commemorate the 250th birthday of Lafayette, let us not forget that the struggle for liberty often brings very different people together to fight for a common cause. Both Washington and Lafayette sacrificed a great deal—risking their lives—to achieve something that probably even surpassed their own expectations.

In a world that seems so full of strife, where so many people are still without freedom, Washington and Lafayette continue to be deserving of our respect, and worthy of our emulation.

James C. Rees
Executive Director
The Mount Vernon Ladies' Association

Lenders to the Exhibition

Mount Vernon extends its gratitude to the many generous lenders, both public and private, who are sharing their treasures for this traveling exhibition: Albert H. Small Declaration of Independence Collection, Special Collections, University of Virginia Library; Anonymous; Clare Edwards; Corcoran Gallery of Art; Cornell University Library; David Bishop Skillman Library, Lafayette College; Diplomatic Reception Rooms, U.S. Department of State; Fondation Josée et René de Chambrun; Fort Ligonier Association; Gilcrease Museum; The Gilder Lehrman Collection, courtesy of the Gilder Lehrman Institute of American History; Henry Francis DuPont Winterthur Museum; Herbert F. Johnson Museum of Art, Cornell University; Historical Society of Pennsylvania Collection, Atwater Kent Museum of Philadelphia; The Kiplinger family; Lafayette College Art Collection; Manuscripts Division, Library of Congress; Maryland Historical Society; Massachusetts Historical Society; Mr. and Mrs. E. Kimbark MacColl; The Morgan Library & Museum; Mount Vernon Ladies' Association; Museum of Early Southern Decorative Arts; New-York Historical Society; Old Sturbridge Village; Ornithology Department, Museum of Comparative Zoology, Harvard College; The Shriners Hospitals for Children and The Masonic Charity Foundation of Connecticut; Society of the Cincinnati, Anderson House; Tudor Place Historic House and Garden; The Valentine Richmond History Center; and Washington and Lee University.

Photography Credits

Cornell University: 6, 53; Fort Ligonier: 55; Gavin Ashworth: 38, 39, 44, 67, 105, 106; Gilcrease Museum: 7, 26; Gilder Lehrman Collection: 33; Hal Conroy: 107; Harvard University: 68; Lafayette College: 8, 22, 23, 31, 36, 58, 59, 61, 63, 65, 76, 77, 80, 81, 82, 86, 88, 97, 99, 101, 102, 108, 124; Library of Congress: 62; Mark Gulezian: 40; Maryland Historical Society: cover; Massachusetts Historical Society: 42; Museum of Early Southern Decorative Arts: 84, 85; Mount Vernon Collection: 3, 24, 25, 37, 48, 54, 60, 64, 72, 116; Old Sturbridge Village: 96; Paul Kennedy: 16; The Pierpont Morgan Library: 52; Peter Leach: 49; Society of the Cincinnati: 87, 104; Taylor Lewis: 46; United States Department of State: 79; The Valentine Richmond History Center: 119; and Washington and Lee University: 56.

"My Beloved General"

THE MARQUIS DE LAFAYETTE'S FILIAL FRIENDSHIP
WITH GEORGE WASHINGTON

In the gracious central passage at Mount Vernon hangs a small elegant vitrine containing a large iron key. The place of honor accorded this artifact is explained by a letter, written March 17, 1790, by the Marquis de Lafayette to George Washington. With this letter Lafayette sent Washington the key to the Bastille, "that fortress of despotism," which Lafayette had ordered razed in the early days of the French Revolution as head of the Paris National Guard. "It is a tribute," he wrote, "Which I owe as A Son to My Adoptive father, as an aid de Camp to My General, as a Missionary of liberty to its patriarch." Lafayette had entrusted the American patriot Thomas Paine with his gift for Washington, and in forwarding the key on to the American president, Paine gave further voice to its significance: "That the principles of America opened the Bastile [sic] is not to be doubted, and therefore the Key comes to the right place."[1]

It is hard to imagine a more fitting symbol than this key for what has come to be known as "the age of democratic revolutions." It links the wellsprings of democracy that emerged in America in 1776 with the stirrings of liberty emanating from France in 1789. It ties together the American "Father of His Country," Washington, with the French "Hero of Two Worlds," Lafayette. And it serves as a tangible embodiment of French-American relations. It is an international symbol connecting democratic ideals, heroes, and nations. But underneath all the trappings of symbolism, it also represents a remarkable friendship, a personal bond between two very human men who loved each other like father and son.

It seemed an unlikely pairing at the beginning—the eager nineteen-year-old French nobleman and the austere forty-five-year-old American commander in chief of an army of ragged insurgents. But the friendship blossomed quickly after their first meeting and endured until Washington's death in 1799. To understand what it was about the young marquis that so endeared him to

At left: The central passage in the Mount Vernon Mansion features the original key to the Bastille and a sketch in pen, ink, and wash of the dilapidated prison, both given to George Washington by the Marquis de Lafayette.

Washington, and that would lead Washington to declare "I do most devoutly wish that we had not a single Foreigner among us, except the Marquis de la Fayette, who acts upon very different principles than those which govern the rest," it is important to understand something about the life and character of Lafayette and the circumstances under which he came to America.[2]

Born in the Auvergne region of France on September 6, 1757, young Gilbert du Motier became the Marquis de Lafayette at the age of two when his father was killed by the British at the Battle of Minden during the Seven Years' War. Lafayette left the family estate, Chavaniac, in 1768 to join his mother and grandfather in Paris, and, with their deaths only weeks apart in 1770, became a very well-to-do orphan. Military service with the King's Musketeers and the Noailles Dragoons soon followed, and he further cemented his relationship with the powerful Noailles family by marrying fourteen-year-old Adrienne de Noailles, daughter of the Duc d'Ayen, in 1774.[3]

Lafayette may have first learned about the revolt of the American colonies in the summer of 1775 at a dinner given by the Comte de Broglie for the Duke of Gloucester, the brother of King George III, who was an outspoken supporter of the colonists. Lafayette, by then a captain in the Noailles Dragoons, was posted in Metz serving under Broglie's command. As a junior officer, he attended the dinner and listened to the enthusiasm of both Broglie and the duke for the American cause. A year-and-a-half later in December of 1776, Lafayette secretly signed an agreement to go to America. The arrangements were made through Silas Deane, the agent for the American colonies in Paris, who was eagerly handing out commissions to French officers and who was particularly taken with the young marquis. Deane agreed to Lafayette's request for the highest rank available—a major generalship—and even more readily to Lafayette's insistence that his service be without pay.

On April 20, 1777, with a new motto for his coat-of-arms—"Cur Non?" (Why Not?)—and in direct defiance of the orders of the king of France and the wishes of his father-in-law, Lafayette and fifteen other officers embarked for America on board the *Victoire*, a ship purchased by Lafayette for the journey. Seasickness, military studies, and English lessons occupied him for much of the dreary two-month voyage. He also penned an extended letter of apology to his pregnant wife, Adrienne, whom he had not told he was going to America. "I trust that, for my sake, you will become a good American," he wrote as the *Victoire* neared the coast of South Carolina. "The welfare of America is intimately connected with the happiness of all mankind; she will become the respectable and safe asylum of virtue, integrity, tolerance, equality, and a peaceful liberty."[4]

Making landfall near Georgetown, South Carolina, Lafayette and his companions were soon on their way to Philadelphia, seat of the Continental Congress. Despite the long, obstacle-fraught journey, Lafayette's spirits remained high; one of his fellow officers observed that "Lafayette's enthusiasm would have sustained anyone who had less than he." The group reached Philadelphia on July 27 and immediately presented themselves to John Hancock and other representatives of Congress, only to be met with a stinging rebuff. Congress, already testy with the war progressing badly, was besieged by foreign officers seeking high-ranking commissions and was in no mood for yet another contingent. Astounded though they were, the Frenchmen continued to press their case until Congress agreed to honor the petition of Lafayette at least. Citing his "zeal, illustrious family and connexions," Congress awarded him the rank of major general, but with the understanding that it was only an honorary post and that he would not be entitled to command a division.[5]

In his negotiations with Congress, Lafayette had expressed the desire to serve with General Washington, and, on July 31, the very day he received his commission and sash, he met George Washington for the first time.[6] The occasion was a dinner in Washington's honor at the Philadelphia City Tavern. Lafayette recognized him immediately: "Although he was surrounded by officers and citizens, the majesty of his figure and his height were unmistakable." For his part, Washington, who had been expecting another irritating French adventurer, was pleasantly surprised by the earnest young officer. Lafayette's enthusiasm for the cause, his manners, modesty, and eagerness to learn English quickly won over the commanding general, who took Lafayette aside and invited him to become a member of his military family. As Lafayette wrote later, "it was with such simplicity that two friends were united whose attachment and confidence were cemented by the greatest of all causes."[7]

In the week that followed, Lafayette joined Washington for an inspection of the Delaware River fortifications and a review of the Continental troops at Germantown, near Philadelphia. Lafayette described the latter in his memoir as a "singular spectacle"—"eleven thousand men, poorly armed and even more poorly clothed." Washington expressed embarrassment at having someone familiar with the polish of the French military see such an army. "I am here to learn, and not to teach," Lafayette tactfully told Washington.[8]

Although elated by his warm welcome at Washington's headquarters, Lafayette continued to press Washington for an independent command for himself and to lobby both Washington and Congress on behalf of his fellow French officers. Washington's bafflement about Congress's intentions regarding Lafayette was expressed in a letter to fellow Virginian Benjamin Harrison, a member of Congress: "What the designs of Congress respecting this Gentn. were—& what line of Conduct I am to pursue, to comply with their design, & his expectations, I know no more than the Child unborn, & beg to be instructed. If Congress meant that this Rank should be unaccompanied by Command I wish it had been sufficiently explain'd to him. If on the other hand, it was intended to vest him with all the powers of a Major Genl., why have I been led into a contrary belief, & left in the dark with respect to my own conduct towards him?"[9]

Lafayette's case was helped by the arrival of letters to Congress from Benjamin Franklin and Silas Deane, indicating that a cordial reception of the well-connected and wealthy nobleman would be beneficial to American interests, but even so, Congress was not yet willing to grant Lafayette a command. Washington, meanwhile, continued to assure him of his own personal regard and esteem. In what Lafayette would later call the "great conversation," Washington told Lafayette to look upon him as a father and friend.[10] Lafayette took this very much to heart from this point forward.

As an aide-de-camp to Washington, Lafayette was one of several young officers for whom the childless Washington nurtured a fatherly affection. Both Alexander Hamilton and John Laurens were among this group, but it was Lafayette who elicited Washington's tenderest feelings. Among these surrogate sons, the ordinarily taciturn commander in chief could relax in the evenings, sharing wine and stories.[11] As for Lafayette, he slipped easily into his place at Washington's headquarters, and with his deference and charm quickly won over the other officers, including Hamilton and Laurens, with whom he formed close friendships. His special relationship with Washington seldom seemed to incite envy among his fellow officers, another indication of his exceptional popularity.[12] Lafayette's success with Americans and Washington in particular owed much to the fact that, unlike many of his countrymen, he was not condescending about American ways and he did not expect American leaders to conform to European conventions. Instead, he was courteous and sympathetic.[13] Lafayette also prized listening and he considered Washington his greatest teacher. "I schall conduct myself entirely by your advices," he told the commander in chief, "and if You say that some thing is proper I'l do it directly—I desire only to know your opinion." Lafayette's philosophy of listening and learning was perhaps best expressed in a letter to his father-in-law in December of 1777: "I read, I study, I examine, I listen, I think, and out of all of that I try to form an opinion into which I cram as much common sense as I can."[14]

Just days after his twentieth birthday in September 1777, Lafayette had the chance further to impress Washington and the other American officers, this time with his courage and coolness under fire. On September 11, he was at Washington's side at the Battle of Brandywine. In the late afternoon, he left Washington, joining Lord Stirling's division just as the British attacked. In the close fighting that followed, he attempted to rally General Thomas Conway's brigade, dismounting to assist them with fixing their bayonets, when he was shot just below the calf.[15] Ignoring his wound until blood poured out of his boot, he allowed Washington's personal physician, Dr. John Cochran, to bind it temporarily as the outmaneuvered American troops retreated toward Chester.[16] Even in retreat, Lafayette continued to try to regroup the soldiers, until Washington arrived and ordered him to submit to further medical attention. At midnight, Washington wrote to Congress to report on the battle and cited Lafayette's baptism by fire.

When Washington determined that he could no longer hold Philadelphia and the evacuation of the city began, Lafayette was taken north to the Moravian community of Bethlehem to continue his recuperation. From Bethlehem, he wrote to Adrienne, reassuring her about his wound and proudly describing his relationship with Washington:

Do not be concerned, dear heart, about the care of my wound. All the physicians in America are paying close attention to me. I have a friend who has spoken to them in such a way that I can be assured of the best care. That friend is General Washington. This estimable man, whom I at first admired for his talents and qualities and whom I

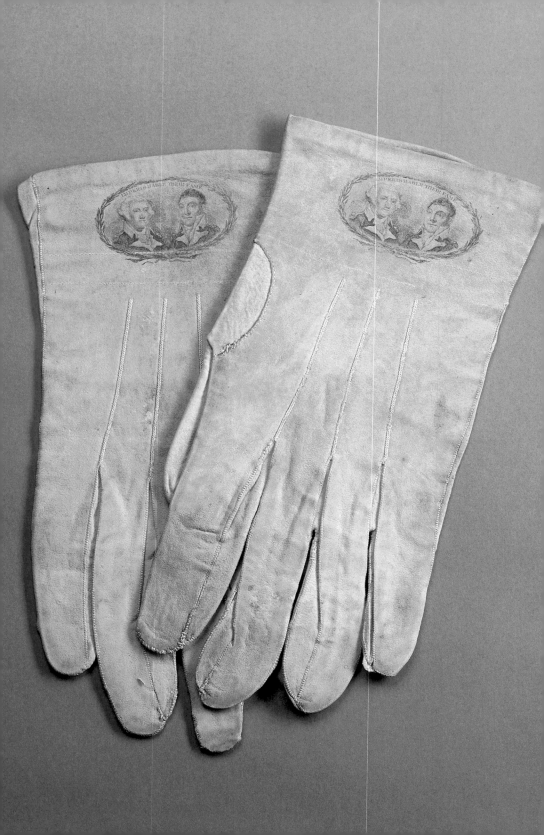

have come to venerate as I know him better, has become my intimate friend. His affectionate interest in me soon won my heart. I am a member of his household and we live together like two brothers in mutual intimacy and confidence. This close friendship makes me as happy as I could possibly be in this country. When he sent his chief surgeon to care for me, he told him to care for me as though I were his son, for he loved me in the same way.

Lafayette also wrote at length to Washington, raising yet again the question of a command. Washington's response was a letter to Congress recommending that a command be considered for Lafayette because of his "illustrious and important connections" and "attachment" to the cause. "Besides," wrote Washington, "he is sensible—discreet in his manners—has made great proficiency in our Language, and from the disposition he discovered at the Battle of Brandy Wine, possesses a large share of bravery and Military ardor."[17]

Lafayette returned to Washington's headquarters in mid-October to a hero's welcome. Although he was still limping, he was eager for more action and asked to accompany General Nathanael Greene on an expedition to Fort Mercer in New Jersey. On November 25, Lafayette took charge of a detachment to observe Lord Cornwallis' camp at Gloucester, and he and his approximately 350 militiamen surprised and routed an outpost of Hessians.

At left and below: Men's gloves featuring an image of Washington and Lafayette, with the inscription "Imperishable Their Fame," kid leather, ca. 1824-1825. David Bishop Skillman Library, Lafayette College.

After accolades from Greene—"The Marquis is determined to be in the way of danger"—and a further entreaty by Washington, Congress acted at last, awarding Lafayette his long-coveted division on December 1.[18]

Lafayette's new command—he selected a division of Virginians in honor of Washington—came just as the army was settling into winter quarters at Valley Forge. Although much of his attention centered on the welfare of his men, he became enmeshed in the misnamed "Conway Cabal," which he believed threatened Washington's leadership as commander in chief. Lafayette's support of Washington was swift and public. "Our general is a man truly made for this revolution, which could not succeed without him," he wrote the Duc d'Ayen. Without Washington, he asked Henry Laurens, president of Congress, "what would become of American liberty? Who could take his place?" To Washington himself, Lafayette pledged his utmost loyalty: "I am now fixed to your fate and I shall follow it and sustain it as well by my sword as by all means in my power." Lafayette later described Washington's demeanor as "the noble calm of a strong and virtuous spirit" and reported that the commander in chief told him: "'I did not seek this position; if I displease the people, I will go, but until then I will resist all intrigue.'"[19]

Mezzotint of George Washington by Charles Willson Peale, 1787. The Mount Vernon Ladies' Association.

In the winter of 1778, Congress assigned Lafayette command of an expedition to invade Canada. Arriving at Albany, New York, to take charge, Lafayette soon realized he had been misled by the Board of War. He found fewer than half of the soldiers he had been promised and most of these had not been paid. Nor was there nearly enough food, clothing, or ammunition. After a valiant effort to try to pull together men and supplies, Lafayette finally had to admit that the obstacles to such an expedition were insurmountable. Disgusted, he wrote Washington: "Why am I so far from you, and what business had that board of war to hurry me through the ice and snow without knowing what I schould do, neither what they were doing themselves? . . . Your excellency may judge that I am very distressed by that disapointement . . . I am affraïd it will reflect on my reputation and I schall be laughed at." Washington responded reassuringly:

> You seem to apprehend that censure proportioned to the disappointed expectations of the World, will fall on you in consequence of the failure of the Canadian Expedition. But in the first, place, it will be no disadvantage to you to have it known in Europe, that you had received so manifest a proof of the good opinion and confidence of Congress, as an important detached Command—and I am persuaded that everyone will applaud your prudence in renouncing a Project, in pursuing which you would vainly have attempted Physical Impossibilities . . . However sensibly your ardour for Glory may make you feel this disappointment, you may be assured that your Character stands as fair as ever it did, and that no new Enterprise is necessary to wipe off this imaginary stain.[20]

Lafayette gratefully rejoined Washington at Valley Forge in April. He arrived just in time to celebrate the signing of the Franco-American treaty of alliance that would bring France into the war on America's side. In mid-May, Lafayette, at the head of a reconnaissance force, was very nearly trapped by the British at Barren Hill. His clever escape embarrassed the British and led Washington to declare, "Upon the whole, the Marquis came handsomely off."[21] Lafayette's part in the Battle of Monmouth in New Jersey on June 28 was less glorious, in part, because of the actions of General Charles Lee. Lee took command of the advance force from Lafayette and bungled an attack, allowing a general retreat just as Washington arrived with the main force. Furious, Washington

Mezzotint of the Marquis de Lafayette by Charles Willson Peale, 1787. The Mount Vernon Ladies' Association.

sent Lee to the rear and took charge himself, ultimately regaining position and forcing the British back toward Monmouth. "During this whole business, which was so badly prepared but ended so well," Lafayette later wrote, "General Washington seemed to arrest fate with a single glance. His nobility, grace, and presence of mind were never displayed to better advantage."[22] Exhausted from the all-day battle in the blazing heat, Washington and Lafayette

rested together in the evening on the same cloak.

With the arrival of the French naval expeditionary force under the Comte d'Estaing in the summer of 1778, Washington sent Lafayette to Rhode Island to serve as liaison between the French and American forces. It was not an easy role. D'Estaing and General John Sullivan, commander of the American forces in Rhode Island, were at odds over tactics, and storms worsened the situation by damaging the French ships. Although Lafayette worked assiduously to soothe feelings on both sides, the allied plan to recapture Newport from the British never came together. Washington ended up having to soothe Lafayette's feelings, which were much ruffled by some American comments about the French. "Every body, Sir, who reasons, will acknowledge the advantages which we have derived from the French Fleet, & the Zeal of the Commander of it," wrote Washington, "but in a free, & republican Government, you cannot restrain the voice of the multitude. Every Man will speak as he thinks, or more properly without thinking . . . Let me beseech you therefore my good Sir to afford a healing hand to the wound that, unintentionally, has been made. America esteems your Virtues & yr. Services and admires the principles upon which you act."[23]

In September, Lafayette requested permission to return home to France on furlough to see his family. Congress not only granted his request but also arranged for a ceremonial sword to be presented to him. Late that fall, Lafayette and Washington said their "tender and painful" farewells. Musing on their parting later in France, Lafayette expressed strong sentiments about his friend: "If he had been a simple soldier, he would have been the bravest one; if he had been an obscure citizen, all his neighbors would have respected him. With a just heart and a just mind, he judged all matters impartially. In creating him expressly for that revolution, nature did great honor to herself." Writing to Lafayette in France, Washington was no less effusive: "Your forward Zeal in the cause of liberty—Your singular attachment to this infant world—Your ardent & persevering efforts not only in America but since your return to France to serve the United States—your polite attention to Americans—and your strict & uniform friendship for me, has ripened the first impressions of esteem & attachment which I imbibed for you into perfect love & gratitude

At left, detail of Washington and Lafayette at the Battle of Brandywine *by John Vanderlyn, oil on canvas, ca. 1825, from the collection of the Gilcrease Museum, Tulsa, Oklahoma.*

that neither time nor absence can impair."[24]

Lafayette was welcomed back to France as a returning hero, even though the king insisted on a week of house arrest for his disobedience in going to America in the first place. After some months spent at Le Havre preparing for a French invasion of England that never materialized, Lafayette set his sights on leading an expeditionary force to America. The French foreign minister, the Comte de Vergennes, finally agreed to send such a force, but chose the older, more experienced, and higher ranking Comte de Rochambeau to lead it. It was decided that Lafayette would resume his old command in the Continental Army. He was dispatched to America to deliver to Washington the secret news of the deployment of the French force, as well as to announce future shipments of clothing and arms that he had helped to procure. On the personal side, Lafayette also brought word of a new son, born December 24, 1779, whom he had named George Washington Lafayette.

Lafayette's arrival in Boston in April 1780 touched off a celebration—a far cry from his reception in 1777. He was now a leading player in the joint alliance that would finally bring an end to the conflict. He had briefed the French on how to act around Americans—"We must not be stingy with cannon salutes" was one bit of advice—and he would do the same for the Americans.[25] Lafayette now hastened to join Washington at Morristown, New Jersey, to deliver his good news. Washington, who had missed Lafayette greatly and had written some remarkably affectionate and amusing letters to him in France, was overjoyed by both the message and the messenger. He immediately named Lafayette as his liaison to Rochambeau and the naval commander, the Chevalier de Ternay. Lafayette served tirelessly in this and myriad other ways on behalf of the alliance. Washington did not exaggerate when he wrote to Congress that Lafayette "has been upon all occasions an essential friend to America."[26]

In the late summer and fall of 1780, chafing at the lack of military action, Lafayette proposed various plans to Washington: "I think it very important, Nay I might Say polically [sic] Necessary that Some thing Brillant Be at this time perform'd By our troops." Washington found he had to counter the eager major general's schemes with a dose of realism: "It is impossible my Dear Marquis to desire more ardently than I do to terminate the campaign by some happy stroke; but we must consult our means rather than our wishes, and not endeavor to better our affairs by attempting things, which for want of success may make them worse."[27]

The opportunity for action presented itself in February 1781, when Lafayette was given charge of an expedition to capture the traitorous Benedict Arnold in Virginia.[28] Leaving his troops in Annapolis, Lafayette went on ahead into Virginia to arrange for transportation and provisions, proving himself a highly skilled negotiator at this task. Returning to Annapolis, he made a detour to visit Washington's mother in Fredericksburg, Virginia, and then stopped briefly to see Mount Vernon for the first time. Mount Vernon was very much on his mind again only weeks later when he learned that Washington's relative and estate manager, Lund Washington, had taken provisions on board a British warship on the Potomac in gratitude for Mount Vernon's reprieve from burning. "Great Happiness is derived from friendship . . . ," he wrote Washington in relating the incident, "But friendship Has its duties, and the Man that Likes you the Best will Be the forwardest in Letting you know Every thing where You Can Be Concerned." Washington, who had learned about the incident already from Lund Washington himself, thanked Lafayette—"The freedom of your communication is an evidence to me of the sincerety of your attachment"—and enclosed a copy of his response to his manager in which his distress was made abundantly clear: "It would have been a less painful circumstance to me, to have heard, that in consequence of your non-compliance with their request, they had burnt my House, and laid the Plantation in ruins."[29]

Although Lafayette's expedition against Arnold was called off for logistical reasons, it marked the beginning of his involvement in Virginia that would culminate in the Yorktown campaign. In April, Lafayette's forces played gadfly to the much larger British force under Arnold's successor, General William Phillips, the same artillery officer whose cannons had killed Lafayette's father at the Battle of Minden in 1759. The arrival of Lord Cornwallis' army from North Carolina in May signaled the British intention to make Virginia a major theater of the war. Although his forces were badly outnumbered, Lafayette, who was commanding the main Continental force in the state, was "determined to Skarmish," as he wrote Washington, "But not to engage too far." Lafayette had a healthy respect for Cornwallis. "This devil Cornwallis is much wiser than the other generals with whom I have dealt," he wrote to his brother-in-law, the Vicomte de Noailles. "He inspires me with a sincere fear, and his name has greatly troubled my sleep. This campaign is a good school for me. God grant that the public does not pay for my lessons."[30]

As both sides reinforced, and Cornwallis moved out of the interior of Virginia toward Yorktown with Lafayette on his heels, the stage was suddenly set for a combined land-sea operation that would trap the British on the Yorktown peninsula. Lafayette's role was to keep Cornwallis from escaping until the French fleet, under Admiral de Grasse, reached the Chesapeake from the West Indies and Washington's and Rochambeau's armies arrived from New York. The tension and excitement of those days were apparent in Washington's communiqués to Lafayette: "If you get anything New from any quarter, send it I pray you on the Spur of Speed; for I am almost all impatience & anxiety."[31] Miraculously, it all came together: de Grasse sailed into the Chesapeake with thirty ships on August 29 and Washington and Rochambeau reached Williamsburg on September 14. A witness reported that when Washington arrived in camp, Lafayette "rode up with precipitation, clasped the General in his arms, and embraced him with an ardor not easily described."[32] After a short siege, Cornwallis surrendered on October 19. "The play is over," wrote Lafayette to the French minister, the Comte de Maurepas, ". . . the fifth act has just ended. I was a bit uneasy during the first acts, but my heart keenly enjoyed the last one."[33]

Determining that there was nothing further he could do before the army went into winter quarters, Lafayette again asked for leave to return to France. He sailed from Boston on December 23 and hurriedly scribbled a postscript to his final letter to Washington: "My last Adieu I must dedicate to My Beloved General. Adieu, My dear General, I know your Heart So well that I am Sure no distance Can alter Your attachment to me."[34] Hailed upon his return to France as the "Hero of Two Worlds," Lafayette immediately set to work arranging for loans and supplies for his adoptive country. When the British opened peace talks, he ably assisted the American Peace Commissioners with negotiations at Versailles.

With the signing of the preliminary peace treaty on January 20, 1783, Lafayette was given the honor of sending the news to Washington. Lafayette's remarkable letter of February 5 to Washington began on a note of triumph:

Were You But Such a Man as Julius Caesar or the king of Prussia, I Should

D'après le physionotrace de Quenedey. Ed.e Gosselin sculp.t 1895.

Gilbert Motier Marquis de
LA FAYETTE.

Aquatint of Lafayette by Gosselin, after Quenedey, 1895.
David Bishop Skillman Library, Lafayette College.

Almost Be Sorry for You at the End of the Great tragedy Where You are Acting Such a Part. But With My dear General I Rejoice at the Blessings of a Peace where our Noble Ends Have Been Secured . . . I Cannot But Envy the Happiness of My Grand Children When they Will Be about Celebrating and Worshipping Your Name—to Have Had One of their Ancestors Among Your Soldiers to know He Had the Good fortune to Be the friend of Your Heart, Will Be the Eternal Honour in Which they Shall Glory.

Then Lafayette made his friend an unexpected proposal, concerning "the Black Part of Mankind." The proposal involved Lafayette and Washington's joint purchase of an estate where they might try an experiment in gradual emancipation—freeing slaves and allowing them to work the land as tenants. Lafayette knew that Washington's example would have great influence on others in America. Promising to lend his own support to making such a plan work in the West Indies, he told Washington: "If it Be a Wild Scheme, I Had Rather Be Mad that Way, than to Be thought Wise on the other tack." Washington responded that Lafayette's plan was "a striking evidence of the benevolence of your Heart. I shall be happy to join you in so laudable a work; but will defer going into a detail of the business, till I have the pleasure of seeing you."[35]

With the end of the American Revolution, Lafayette turned his energies to promoting the economic interests of America in France. He also avidly followed the news from America, particularly as it related to Washington. "Your Circular letter, My dear General, as well as Your Modest Retirement," wrote Lafayette, "Have Had the Universal Applause of Europe." Lafayette also agreed to Washington's request that he head the French branch of the newly-formed Society of the Cincinnati, an association for officers in the Continental and French armies who had served in America for three years or more. The hereditary succession established for membership, passing from eldest son to eldest son, was highly controversial in America because of fears it would create an American aristocracy. "If it is found that the Heredity Endangers the true principles of democraty [sic]," Lafayette wrote Washington, "I am as Ready as Any Man to Renounce it. You Will Be My Compass." Despite the fact that Washington, as president of the American branch, did choose to oppose the heredity clause, the practice was not relinquished by the Society.[36]

Detail from a letter written by Lafayette to Washington on July 8, 1781, in which he reports his success in deceiving British General Cornwallis. The Gilder Lehrman Collection, courtesy of The Gilder Lehrman Institute of American History [GLC 05467].

In August 1784, Lafayette returned to America for a four-and-a-half-month visit. Throngs of Americans cheered his every move through ten states. He addressed the Continental Congress as well as six state legislatures on the importance of a strong federal union, and he played a vital role in the peace negotiations with the Iroquois at Fort Schuyler in New York. The highlight of his visit was his August reunion with Washington at Mount Vernon. "I assure you that in retirement General Washington is even greater than he was during the Revolution," he wrote Adrienne. "His simplicity is truly sublime, and he is as completely involved with all the details of his lands and house as if he had always lived here."[37] In November, Lafayette met Washington in Richmond for several days of civic celebrations; then, returning with the general to Mount Vernon, Lafayette said his goodbyes to Washington's extended family to whom he had become quite attached. Washington, in turn, gave Lafayette a letter for Adrienne in which he told her: "The Marquis returns to you with all the warmth & ardour of a newly inspired lover—we restore him to you in good health, crowned with wreaths of love & respect from every part of the Union."[38]

Washington accompanied Lafayette on his journey north as far as Annapolis, where on December 1 the two said their final farewells. Sensing, correctly as it turned out, that this would be their last meeting, Washington wrote to Lafayette: "In the moment of our separation upon the road as I travelled, & every hour since—I felt all that love, respect & attachment for you, with which length of years, close connexion & your merits, have inspired me. I often asked myself, as our Carriages distended, whether that was the last sight, I ever should have of you? And tho' I wished to say no—my fears answered yes." Lafayette responded passionately: "No, my Beloved General, our late parting was Not By Any Means a last interview—My whole Soul Revolts at the idea . . . Adieu, adieu, My dear General, it is with Unexpressible pain that I feel I am Going to be Severed from You By the atlantick—Every thing that Admiration, Respect, Gratitude, friendship, and filial love Can inspire, is Combined in my Affectionate Heart to devote me most tenderly to You—in your friendship I find a Delight which words Cannot Express—adieu my dear general."[39]

In the years that followed, affectionate letters as well as gifts—Virginia hams, French dolls, seeds, birds, and even jackasses—flowed back and forth across the Atlantic between the Lafayettes and the Washingtons. Lafayette sent Washington a family portrait, which Washington pronounced "an invaluable present," to be given "the best place in my House."[40] Lafayette wrote to Washington about his work to secure rights for French Protestants and to promote the abolition of slavery, confiding that he had purchased a plantation in the French colony of Cayenne [present-day French Guiana] in South America to try his experiment in emancipating slaves.[41] Washington called the Cayenne venture "generous and noble proof of your humanity. Would to God a like spirit would diffuse itself generally into the minds of the people of this country, but I despair of seeing it."[42]

Beginning in 1787, Lafayette's letters are filled with news of the unfolding events in France that would lead to full-scale revolution in 1789: "The spirit of liberty is prevailing in this Country at a Great Rate—liberal ideas are Cantering about from one end of the Kingdom to the other."[43] Washington sent Lafayette a copy of the new American Constitution, over whose birth he had presided as chair of the Constitutional Convention. "It is now a Child of fortune," he wrote to Lafayette, "to be fostered by some and buffited by others."[44] Lafayette responded with admiration, calling it a "Bold, large, and solid frame for the Confederation." His two concerns, the "want of a declaration of Rights" and the "Great powers and possible Continuance of the president," he believed could be remedied, especially if Washington would assume the presidency—"in the Name of America, of Mankind at large, and Your Own fame, I Beseech you, my dear General, Not to deny your Acceptance of the office of president for the first Years."[45] Washington professed his characteristic reluctance: "In answer to the observations you make on the probability of my election to the Presidency (knowing me as you do) I need only say, that it has no enticing charms, and no fascinating allurements for me . . . Let those follow the pursuits of ambition and fame, who have a keener relish for them."[46]

Lafayette's letters to Washington grew less frequent as he became swept up in the events in France. As primary author of the Declaration of the Rights of Man (modeled on the American Declaration of Independence) and as commandant of the Paris National Guard, Lafayette's role in the early days of the French Revolution was large. However, his moderate position as a constitutional monarchist was soon threatened by the radical, anti-monarchist Jacobins. Washington's fears for Lafayette's safety, which he expressed in his letters, proved prescient. With the arrest of Louis XVI in the summer of 1792, Lafayette attempted to escape to America, but was captured at the Belgian border by the Austrians, who were then at war with France. Imprisoned for five years in Prussia and Austria, he was joined for the last two years at the Fortress of Olmütz by his wife and daughters, who voluntarily chose to endure his captivity rather than be separated from him. Adrienne, who had only narrowly escaped the guillotine herself, had managed to spirit George Washington Lafayette to America to be placed under Washington's protection.

Both Lafayette's captivity and his son's arrival in America in 1795 put Washington in a politically awkward position. As much as he wished to help Lafayette, as President of the United States he was committed to a policy of strict neutrality toward France and her enemies. Hence, his activities on behalf of Lafayette were carried out behind the scenes; he sent some of his own funds to Adrienne and made private appeals to the emperors of Prussia and Austria for Lafayette's release. He asked Secretary of State Thomas Jefferson to instruct the American minister to France, Gouverneur Morris, "to neglect no favorable opportunity of expressing *informally* the sentiments & wishes of this Country respecting M. de la Fayette." And he further admonished Jefferson to convey on his behalf to "Madame de la Fayette . . . all the consolation I can

Engraving of Lafayette and his family at the prison of Olmütz, E. Henne, after drawing by P. C. D'Agrain. David Bishop Skillman Library, Lafayette College.

with propriety give her consistent with my public character & the National policy."[47] Through Alexander Hamilton, Washington arranged for George Washington Lafayette to live in New York for several months after his arrival, but anguished over the need to keep him at arm's length. "Have you seen or heard more of young Fayette since you last wrote to me on that subject?" he asked Hamilton. "Where did he go to? Did you deliver him the letter I sent under cover to you for him? His case gives me pain, and I do not know how to get relieved from it."[48]

Ultimately Washington brought George Washington Lafayette into the presidential household in Philadelphia, and, when he retired in early 1797, the boy accompanied him back to Mount Vernon. When word came of the impending release of the "Prisoners of Olmütz" in the fall of 1797, young George rushed back to Europe, carrying with him a warm letter from Washington to Lafayette. After rejoicing over Lafayette's release and praising the conduct of his son, Washington reported on his own retirement from public life: "I have once more retreated to the shades of my own Vine and Fig tree, where I shall remain with best vows for the prosperity of that country for whose happiness I have toiled many years, to establish its Independence—Constitution & Laws—and for the good of mankind in general, until the days of my sojournment, wh[ic]h cannot be many, are accomplished."[49]

It was just after his return from exile to France in January 1800 that

G. WASHINGTON *in his last Illness attended by Doc.ʳˢ Craik and Brown*

Americans behold & shed a grateful Tear | *And now is departing unto the realms above*
for a man who has gained yoᵘ freedom most dear | *Where he may ever rest in lasting peace & love*

*Etching, 1800, of George Washington's last illness, with Doctors Craik and Brown,
as well as Mrs. Washington, in attendance. The Mount Vernon Ladies' Association.*

Lafayette received word of the death of his beloved general on December 14, 1799. In his will, Washington bequeathed to Lafayette "a pair of finely wrought steel pistols, taken from the enemy in the Revolutionary War." As honored as Lafayette must have been by this token of remembrance, he may have been even more moved by another provision of Washington's will. The second clause of the will directed that: "Upon the decease of my wife, it is my Will & desire that all the Slaves which I hold in <u>my own right</u> shall receive their freedom." Moreover, Washington stipulated that upon emancipation, arrangements be made to support the elderly and sick and to educate and train the children for "some useful occupation." He expressly prohibited the sale "of any Slave I may die possessed of, under any pretense whatsoever." And he insisted that his instructions "respecting Slaves . . . be religiously fulfilled . . . without evasion, neglect, or delay."[50]

Commemorative pitcher featuring George Washington and the Marquis de Lafayette (on opposite sides). The Mount Vernon Ladies' Association.

It was an extraordinary document, and in creating it, Washington did what most of his peers would not. His path to this decision was not easy, but undoubtedly one of his guides along the way was Lafayette. For his part, Lafayette remained committed to the anti-slavery movement throughout his life, agonizing as his adopted country continued to hold on to so abhorrent a system. He reportedly expressed his regret to his friend, British abolitionist Thomas Clarkson: "I never would have drawn my sword in the cause of America, if I could have conceived that thereby I was founding a land of slavery."[51]

Lafayette returned to America once more at the invitation of Congress in 1824, as the "Guest of the Nation." From the moment he landed in August 1824, amid a welcoming flotilla at Castle Garden in New York harbor, until his departure in September 1825 with a trunk of American soil for his grave, Lafayette was embraced by the young republic as a venerated symbol of the American Revolution. Everywhere he went during the "Farewell Tour"—and he visited each of the twenty-four states in the Union—he was greeted with an outpouring of national affection. Thousands of Americans turned out to see him in every city, where civic leaders organized elaborate welcome parades, receptions, dinners, and balls in his honor. Accompanied on his journey by George Washington Lafayette and his secretary Auguste Levasseur, Lafayette returned to many Revolutionary War sites, including Brandywine and Bunker Hill. At Yorktown, he celebrated the forty-third anniversary of Cornwallis' surrender, greeting veterans under the very tent used by Washington, which had been pitched especially for the occasion.

Lafayette's friendship with Washington still resonated with Americans in 1824. And they could commemorate it with special souvenir items made in honor of the Farewell Tour—china pitchers and glass flasks with Lafayette's image on one side and Washington's on the other, or silk ribbons and kid gloves bearing likenesses of the two men and the phrase "Lafayette, the Companion of Washington." An especially popular image showed Lafayette at the tomb of Washington, which he had visited at Mount Vernon in October 1824. Lafayette's secretary, Levasseur, wrote poignantly of this visit, describing the arrival of Lafayette's party by steamboat on the Potomac. They were greeted by Washington's relatives, who conducted them to Washington's simple grave. Martha Washington's grandson, George Washington Parke Custis, presented Lafayette with a gold ring encasing a lock

This pitcher was crafted by Richard Hall and Sons of Staffordshire, England. The Mount Vernon Ladies' Association.

of the general's hair. The group then spent an hour in the house and gardens. George Washington Lafayette confirmed that the house remained much as he had remembered it from 1797, and he found again the key to the Bastille just where Washington had placed it. "After a few moments of repose," wrote Levasseur,

> we again took the path which leads down to the shore. Our march was a silent one. Each of us bore in his hand a branch of cypress, cut from over the tomb of Washington. We might have seemed an afflicted family, returning from committing to

the earth a father dearly beloved, who had been removed by death. We were already on board, and had proceeded far over the rapid waves, before any person broke the silence of meditation. At length Mount Vernon disappeared behind the winding and elevated banks of the river, when all assembled in the stern of the vessel, and listened attentively until evening, while General Lafayette spoke of Washington.[52]

A decade later, Americans again commemorated Lafayette with ringing bells and swags of bunting, but this time the bells were muffled and the bunting was black. Word had come of Lafayette's death in Paris on May 20, 1834, and the nation plunged into mourning. By order of President Andrew Jackson, Lafayette was accorded the same military honors that had been given to Washington thirty-four years before. Congress draped its chambers in crepe, and former president John Quincy Adams delivered a three-hour eulogy at a joint session. In cities and towns across America, citizens gathered to say farewell to the "Companion of Washington" with eulogies, songs, and poetry. Lafayette was laid to rest in the small Parisian cemetery of Picpus, under the soil brought back from Bunker Hill. Today, as it has since 1834, an American flag flies over the grave, and each year on July 4th, the American ambassador to France leads a delegation of Americans who come to pay their respects to the "Hero of Two Worlds."

Diane Windham Shaw
Lafayette College
February 1, 2006

At left, detail of Lafayette at the tomb of Washington, print by Nathaniel Currier, 1845. The Mount Vernon Ladies' Association.

Gilbert du Motier, Marquis de Lafayette by Joseph Boze, oil on canvas, ca. 1790.
Courtesy of the Massachusetts Historical Society.

SECTION I

A Missionary of Liberty
1777-1799

"Never before had such a glorious cause attracted the attention of mankind; it was the final struggle of liberty, and its defeat would have left it neither asylum nor hope. . . . When I first learned of [the Revolutionary War], my heart was enlisted, and I thought only of joining the colors."[1] These words, written by Marie Joseph Paul Yves Roch Gilbert du Motier, Marquis de Lafayette, in his *Mémoires*, summarize his passionate interest in joining the American fight for independence. Stirred to action, Lafayette sailed for America on April 20, 1777; the nineteen-year-old French nobleman spoke no English but studied the language on his journey.

Landing in South Carolina on June 13, 1777, Lafayette traveled to Philadelphia to request an appointment to the American army from the Continental Congress. Lafayette reported that Congress' first reaction was dismissive. However, he persisted and gained their attention—along with a commission to the rank of major general—by asserting that he would serve at his own expense (as did Washington). Although he did not yet have command of troops, Lafayette became the highest ranking foreigner to serve in the Continental Army.

Lafayette similarly persisted and ultimately succeeded in gaining favor with George Washington, who, like Congress, was wary of the many foreign adventurers seeking commissions. As Lafayette noted, Washington was surrounded by "flatterers and secret enemies."[2]

Although the bond between the two men was not cemented quite so quickly as Lafayette suggests in his memoirs, he soon convinced Washington of the genuineness of his intentions, his character, and his devotion to the cause of American liberty. When later introducing Lafayette to Benjamin Franklin, Washington praised the Frenchman's gallantry and military successes as "such proofs of his Zeal, military ardour and talents as have endeared him to America, . . . I have a very particular friendship for him, . . ."[3] In this same letter, Washington referred to Lafayette being shot at the Battle of Brandywine.

Sèvres tea set Lafayette sent from France to Mrs. Washington's granddaughter, Eliza Parke Custis. The Mount Vernon Ladies' Association.

Lafayette demonstrated his bravery there and in an engagement near Philadelphia, leading Congress to approve Washington's request to give him command of the Eighth Virginia Regiment. Lafayette likely chose this particular command because the men were from Virginia, the home of Washington. Lafayette later served with Washington during the arduous winter at Valley Forge and in battles such as the victory Americans claimed at Monmouth, New Jersey.

While this military service was certainly important, Lafayette's diplomatic efforts on behalf of America and its war effort were invaluable. In January 1779 he sailed from Boston on the aptly-named *Alliance* in order to convince the French government to provide much-needed troops and supplies. Roughly eighteen months later, Lafayette returned to the United States and delivered secret, critical news to Washington: Louis XVI, King of France, had sent more than 6,000 men along with artillery, ships, ammunition, and money to aid the American cause. Washington made clear his gratitude to Lafayette when he wrote Samuel Huntington, President of Congress, citing the *joy I feel at the return of a Gentleman who has distinguished himself in the service of this Country so signally, who has given so many and so decisive proofs of his attachments to its interests, and who ought to be dear to it by every motive. . . . The warm friendship I have for him conspires with considerations of public utility to afford me a double satisfaction in his return. During the time he has been in France he has uniformly manifested the same zeal in our affairs which animated his conduct while he was among us.*[4]

In April 1781 Washington placed Lafayette in charge of military operations in Virginia, where British General Cornwallis had centered his campaign. The British believed that defeating Americans there would crush the revolution and end the war since Virginia was the largest colony and its tobacco was so important in funding the American army.

Lafayette was instrumental in events leading to the decisive American victory at Yorktown. Roughly three months before that final battle, Lafayette described his duty in Virginia to Washington:

Agreeably to Your orders I have avoided a general action [major battle], and when Lord Cornwallis's movements indicated it was against His interest to fight I have ventured partial engagements. . . . It has been a great secret that our Army was not superior and was most generally inferior to the Enemy's numbers.[5]

Lafayette's efforts to keep Cornwallis in Virginia until the American and French armies, in addition to the French naval force, could converge there was an essential ingredient leading to the defeat of the British at Yorktown in October 1781.

One week after the victory, Lafayette wrote from Yorktown:

The Glorious, and important success, we have obtained will afford joy to every true American. . . . The storm that had been gathered against this small Army gave us great deal of trouble to maintain the Vessel afloat. Nothing but the [army's] bravery, fortitude zeal and discipline. . . could have saved us from ruin, and extricated us from our innumerable difficulties. . . . [This victory is] so great in its consequences that it must add a new glory to Genl. Washingtons name and become a new tie of confidence and affection between the two Nations. . . . to see this little affair transacted under the eyes of Foreign Armies, gave me Unspeakable Satisfaction.[6]

Because both Washington and Lafayette realized slavery contradicted the principles of the American Revolution, it was among the many topics they addressed in their ongoing correspondence after Yorktown. Lafayette hoped Washington would follow his lead in an experiment the marquis and his wife,

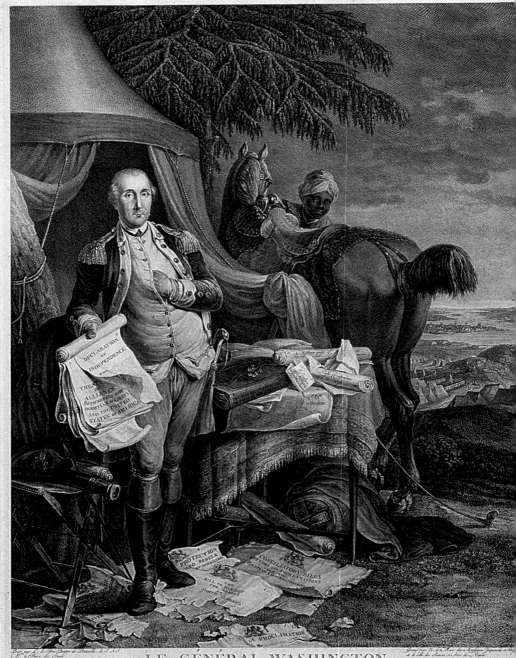

LE GÉNÉRAL WASHINGTON

Ne Quid Detrimenti capiat Res publica.

Gravé d'après le Tableau Original appartenant à Mr. Marquis de la Fayette.

Cette Estampe se Vend avec Privilège du Roy à Paris chez le Mire Graveur rüe et porte St. Jacques, Maison de Mr. le Camus Md. de Drap, prix 12 livres.

Adrienne de Noailles de Lafayette, attempted in what is now known as French Guiana. The Lafayettes purchased land there, began educating the enslaved individuals, and paid them for their work in hopes the experiment would lead to emancipation of slaves there.[7] Lafayette's abolitionist stance was no doubt one of the catalysts in Washington's changing opinion of slavery.

In the same letter outlining this abolitionist experiment, Lafayette informed Washington of the "Prospect of a Peace," or a treaty officially recognizing America's victory in the Revolutionary War. Despite the triumph at Yorktown, Washington had insisted on maintaining military readiness until the peace treaty was signed. To further Washington's goal of continued preparedness, Lafayette worked diligently in Europe to secure maritime superiority by America and her allies, gain financial support, and advance American commercial interests. In one of several letters using a code to guard highly sensitive information, Lafayette wrote of representing Washington's desires "in the Strongest light Imaginable."[8] Washington praised Lafayette's efforts, commenting on his "zeal for the American Cause."[9] Thomas Jefferson, America's minister to France from 1784-1789, recollected that "All doors of all departments were open to [Lafayette] at all times, to me only formally and at appointed times. In truth, I only held the nail, he drove it."[10]

In addition to an ongoing correspondence, Washington, Lafayette, and their families exchanged numerous gifts. The marquis sent Washington golden pheasants from King Louis XVI's stock and later gave a Sèvres tea service to one of Martha Washington's grandchildren. The Frenchman, according to Washington family tradition, gave Washington a ring featuring a portrait of the American general. Washington asked Lafayette to acquire for him several fashionable pieces of French silver-plated wares, noting that he trusted Lafayette's judgment regarding price and workmanship, and that Lafayette knew "our customs, taste and manner of living in America."[11] Letters even carried kisses for members of their family, such as one for Anastasie, Lafayette's daughter, from Washington who had "the pleasure of being her well wisher."[12]

Washington's gifts or favors to Lafayette included seeds of various American plants for Louis XVI's garden; Martha Washington sent to Adrienne a gift of Virginia hams. Washington sent Lafayette a copy of the new United

At left, Le Général Washington, *Noël Le Mire, after Charles Willson Peale, engraving, 1780. The Mount Vernon Ladies' Association.*

States Constitution. Although Lafayette highly praised the new Constitution in a letter to Washington, he noted its lack of a "declaration of Rights" and urged Washington not to refuse becoming the nation's first president, writing: "You only Can settle that political Machine, and I foresee it will furnish An Admirable Chapter in your History."[13]

After an invitation from Washington to visit America, Lafayette returned in 1784 and stayed with his "family" at Mount Vernon for a week. One day after arriving there, he wrote to his wife, Adrienne: "I am. . . reveling in the happiness of finding my dear general again. . . ."[14] This was the last time Washington and Lafayette were together.

Lafayette's reception by the American people during this nearly five-month

On his deathbed, Washington is surrounded by his distraught family, doctors, and house servants. Lithograph published by James Baillie, 19th century. The Mount Vernon Ladies' Association.

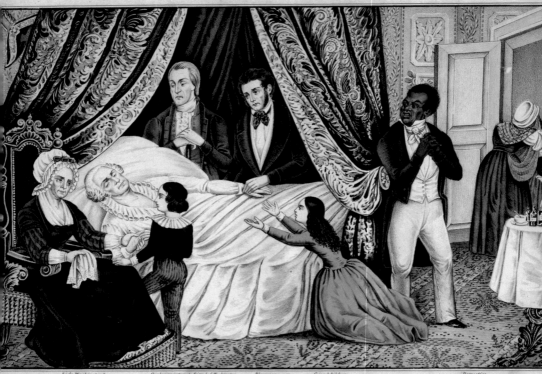

DEATH OF WASHINGTON, Dec. 14. A. D. 1799.

visit foreshadowed his even more remarkable welcome forty years later. James Madison, writing to Thomas Jefferson in 1784, described the scene as "Wherever [Lafayette] passes he receives the most flattering tokens of sincere affection from all ranks."[15] The marquis himself wrote: "Upon viewing Again these Blessed shores of liberty my Heart throbbed for joy, and Nothing Could add to my Satisfaction But the flattering Reception with which I Have Been Every where Honoured."[16] Americans continued to honor Lafayette after his return to France. Virginia, Maryland, Massachusetts, and Connecticut granted him honorary citizenship; the College of William and Mary, Harvard, Princeton, and the University of Pennsylvania gave him honorary degrees.

Above, Detail of a pastel portrait of George Washington Lafayette by James Sharples, 1796-1797. The Mount Vernon Ladies' Association.

Americans saw Lafayette's role in the French Revolution as extending the same principles he and Washington had successfully pursued in the American Revolution. Lafayette was elected to the Estates General, the national legislative body, and on July 11, 1789, he presented to them a draft for the Declaration of the Rights of Man and the Citizen. Modeled partly on the American Declaration of Independence, it too is one of the basic charters of human liberty. The principles of this Declaration helped inspire the French Revolution; its first two articles state: "Men are born and remain free and equal in rights. . ." and "The aim of every political association is the preservation of the natural and imprescriptible rights of man. These rights are Liberty, Property, Safety and Resistance to Oppression."[17] Lafayette planned to display this French Declaration together with the American Declaration of Independence.

Lafayette ordered the demolition of the Bastille, a Paris prison holding political opponents of the government, after it was stormed by Frenchmen on

July 14, 1789. Considering Washington liberty's founding father, Lafayette sent him the main key to the Bastille as well as a sketch of its demolition. The connection between the Washington and Lafayette families was further cemented when Lafayette and his wife entrusted the safety of their fifteen-year-old son, George Washington Lafayette, to the Washingtons during the French Revolution. The young man eventually became a cherished member of the Washington family; he is included in a group of pastel portraits of the family drawn in 1796-1797 by James Sharples.

Lafayette was seen as sympathetic to the French king and queen, and, as the French Revolution became more radical, he fell from popular favor. Under threat of arrest, Lafayette fled but was captured and imprisoned. Adrienne was also arrested as were her grandmother, mother, and sister. While Adrienne escaped the guillotine, these three relatives did not.

Lafayette remained a prisoner from 1792 to 1797. He unsuccessfully argued that he should be released because of his American citizenship, and Washington and Congress tried to win his freedom. Writing to the King of Prussia on January 15, 1794, Washington noted his "personal and affectionate anxiety for the welfare of M. de la Fayette."[18]

The French Revolution bankrupted Lafayette. In order to provide some relief, Congress voted in 1794 to grant him $24,424 as the wages he would have received if he had not volunteered during the American Revolution. However, this was only a fraction of the amount he had spent to help fund and supply the American army. When Lafayette was finally released, President Washington wrote him a letter he hoped would be delivered by his namesake, George Washington Lafayette. The president commented on how richly Lafayette deserved his freedom, reported on the admirable behavior of his son, and closed by writing that "if inclination or events should induce you, or any of [your family], to visit America, no person in it would receive you with more cordiality and affection than Mrs. Washington and myself. . . ."[19]

Washington died just over two years later. This momentous event spurred Lafayette to include this tribute to Washington and his widow in a letter to Alexander Hamilton:

> . . . *Him whose Lamentable Loss to Mankind is to You, to all His personal friends, to Me His Adoptive and Loving Son So desolately deplorable!* . . . *[Lafayette then asks Hamilton to] promote Any proper demand that His Worthy Widow finds Herself By*

Her Situation and the Merits of Her Husband Warranted to Procure . . . .[20]

Lafayette also wrote a letter of condolence to Martha Washington, and, on October 31, 1800, she responded to his "sympathetic and affectionate letter" and enclosed a leaf from Washington's tomb. The leaf features a portrait of the marquis, likely drawn by one of Mrs. Washington's granddaughters. Washington's widow commented on

> *The tribute of respectful veneration which has been every where paid to the memory of my dear deceased Husband, and the tender sympathy which my friends have expressed for the irreparable loss, excites my warmest sensibility. . . . Knowing the strong ties by which you were bound to my departed Friend I can readily conceive of your feeling upon hearing of his decease, and I am sure it was not among the least of the manifold afflictions which you have of late years undergone. . . . be [assured] that you have my ernest [sic] prayers that your and [your family's] future years may be freed from that cloud of suffering in which you have been so long involved——, and that every blessing which heaven has in store for the virtuous may be showered upon you——should you or they visit this country——I need not say how happy I should be to see you under my roof——and it will always afford me the highest satisfaction to hear of your welfare.*[21]

Life mask of George Washington by Jean-Antoine Houdon.

LIFE MASK OF GEORGE WASHINGTON

Jean-Antoine Houdon (1741-1828), French
Plaster, October 1785

LIFE MASK OF LAFAYETTE

Jean-Antoine Houdon (1741-1828), French
Plaster, July 1785

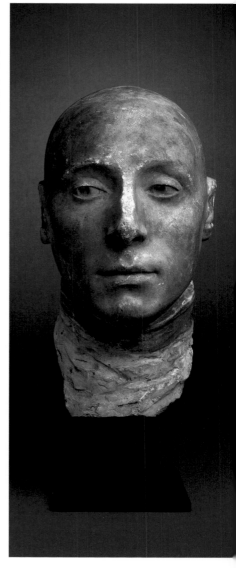

The Virginia legislature unanimously resolved on December 17, 1781, to commission a marble bust of Lafayette in gratitude for his role in the victory at Yorktown. The project was waylaid until the summer of 1785, when the Virginia delegates had also determined to have made a marble statue of General George Washington. The legislature requested that Thomas Jefferson and Benjamin Franklin, acting as agents in Europe, find the best sculptor for these prestigious commissions. Jefferson and Franklin strongly recommended the renowned sculptor Jean-Antoine Houdon who, it was said, "lacks only the means to make his portraits speak, since, as for likeness, he lacks nothing."[22] Houdon's sculptures were incredibly accurate because he took extensive measurements of his subject's features and often created a plaster cast of the face.

The young marquis, already a celebrated war hero, was just twenty-eight when Houdon made this plaster life mask in Paris. A few

Life mask of the Marquis de Lafayette
also by Jean-Antoine Houdon.

months later, Houdon made his first voyage across the ocean to observe the fifty-three-year-old Washington at Mount Vernon, make a life mask, and create a terracotta bust. Using these life masks as reference, Houdon completed two busts of Lafayette—one for the city of Paris and one for the Virginia Capitol—and a full-size sculpture of Washington also for the Capitol in Richmond. Houdon used a mold of the clay bust at Mount Vernon to create numerous masks and busts. The mask of Washington in the Morgan Library's collection is considered the closest to the plaster mask taken at Mount Vernon, while Cornell University's mask of Lafayette reveals the smoothness of his young aristocratic face. Lafayette wrote to Washington in October of 1786, "A New instance of the Goodness of the State of Virginia Has Been Given me, by the placing of My Bust at the Hotel de ville of this City [Paris]—the Situation of the other Bust will Be the More pleasing to Me as While it places me within the Capitol of the State, I will Be eternally By the Side of, and paying an Everlasting Homage to the Statue of My Beloved General."[23]

LAFAYETTE-WASHINGTON-JACKSON PISTOLS

Jacob Walster (active 1761-1790), Saarbruck, France (now Germany) Walnut, steel with gold and silver inlay, ca. 1775-1776

Courtesy of Fort Ligonier Association, Ligonier, Pennsylvania (MVLA)

Lafayette likely purchased these pistols during the two years he was stationed in Metz as a member of the French Royal Army and shortly before his departure to join the battle for liberty in America. He presented the pistols to George Washington during the Revolutionary War as a token of their burgeoning friendship. After Washington's death in 1799, the pistols came into the possession of William

Detail showing President Andrew Jackson from The Presidents of the United States, *designed by Robert W. Weir and engraved by J. W. Casilear, 1834. The Mount Vernon Ladies' Association.*

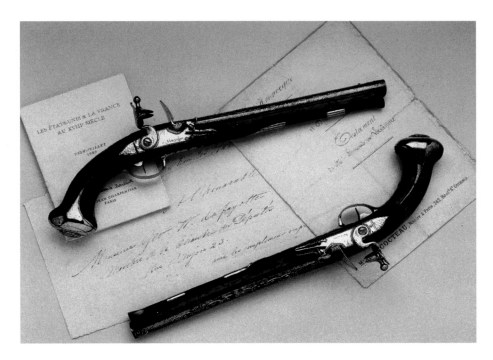

Lafayette presented these pistols to Washington during the American Revolution as a token of their friendship. The pistols later were owned by Andrew Jackson who bequeathed them to George Washington Lafayette.

Robinson, the son-in-law of William Augustine Washington, one of George Washington's favorite nephews. On the eve of Andrew Jackson's run for the presidency, it was Robinson's wish that the pistols be presented to that hero of the War of 1812. Two members of the U.S. House of Representatives made the presentation, including Robinson's friend Colonel Charles Fenton Mercer of Virginia. Mercer concluded his address at the presentation by stating, "In becoming yours, on this day, they [the pistols] are destined to multiply the memorials of the brilliant and extraordinary achievement in the military annals of this eventful age."[24] Because Jackson valued his friendship with Lafayette and respected the historical significance of the pistols, he later bequeathed them to George Washington Lafayette.[25]

Marquis de Lafayette by Charles Willson Peale, commissioned by Washington in 1779.

Marquis de Lafayette

Charles Willson Peale (1741-1827), American
Oil on canvas, 1779

Courtesy of Washington and Lee University, Lexington, Virginia;
Washington-Custis-Lee Collection of Portraits
(MVLA, LC, N-YHS)

George Washington and Charles Willson Peale began a lifelong friendship in 1772 when the painter came to Mount Vernon to complete the life portrait Washington had commissioned. Seven years later, Washington commissioned Peale to paint a portrait of his dear friend, the Marquis de Lafayette. Lafayette, however, was not able to sit for the portrait until the summer of 1780, and, by December of that year, Washington had grown impatient, writing to Peale, "I persuade myself you will embrace the oppertunity [sic] of the Marquis de la Fayette's visit to Philadelphia to give the picture of him the finishing touches. You may not have another oppertunity [sic], and I wish its completion."[26] Peale continued to work on the painting, making "an entire change of the back ground," and Washington finally received the painting depicting Lafayette in his Continental Army uniform in 1781.[27] The probate inventory taken of Mount Vernon after George Washington's death in 1799 indicates that a portrait of Lafayette was hanging in the second-floor bedroom where the Frenchman stayed when he visited the Washingtons in 1784.

Marquis de Lafayette to George Washington, March 30, 1782

Courtesy of David Bishop Skillman Library, Lafayette College
(MVLA)

Washington and Lafayette deftly used codes and other secret methods to send and receive sensitive information during the American Revolution, and, in this letter, Washington has deciphered the code between the lines of Lafayette's letter.

Because the British kept a large and formidable force on American soil following their surrender at Yorktown, Washington maintained an active army and asked Lafayette to secure further financial and military help from France and other European powers in preparing for further battles. Washington particularly sought naval superiority.

Lafayette responded to Washington's request:

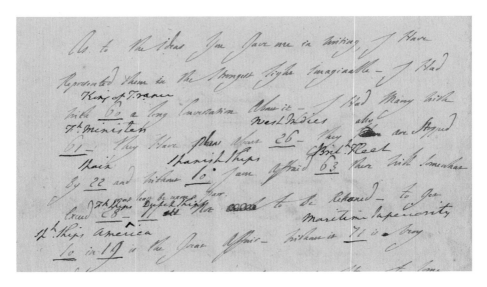

Detail of letter from Lafayette to Washignton, March 30, 1782.

As to the ideas You Gave me in writing [in the letter of January 4], I Have Represented them in the Strongest light Imaginable. I Had With KING OF FRANCE a long Conversation About it. I Had Many With FRENCH MINISTERS. . . . To Get SPANISH SHIPS in AMERICA is the Great Affair. Without it MARITIME SUPERIORITY is Very difficult . . . .[28]

LAFAYETTE AT YORKTOWN

Jean-Baptiste Le Paon (ca. 1738-1785), French
Oil on canvas, ca. 1783-1785

*Gift of Helen Fahnstock Hubbard in Memory of her husband, John Hubbard,
(Harvard class of 1892), 1943. Lafayette College Art Collection, Easton, Pa.
(MVLA, LC, N-YHS)*

GEORGE WASHINGTON

Jean-Baptiste Le Paon (ca. 1738-1785), French, after Charles Willson Peale
(1741-1827), American
Oil on canvas, ca. 1779

*The Mount Vernon Ladies' Association.
Purchased with funds donated by Mr. and Mrs. Guerin Todd, Mr. and Mrs. Donald L. Segur,
Mrs. Lyle C. Roll, Mrs. Samuel M. V. Hamilton, Pendleton Woolen Mills,
Mrs. C. Lalor Burdick, and Mrs. Richard Alexander, 1992
(MVLA, LC, N-YHS)*

Lafayette at Yorktown with his servant James Armistead by Jean-Baptiste Le Paon.

George Washington by Jean-Baptiste Le Paon

Although Jean-Baptiste Le Paon, an artist in the court of Louis XVI, was known for large battle scenes, he painted two portraits during his career. His portrait of George Washington was painted at a time when Europeans, and the French in particular, were eager to know more about the dashing American general. Numerous fictitious portraits of Washington were produced abroad in the early 1770s, but after the American artist Charles Willson Peale completed a life portrait of Washington for John Hancock in 1776, prints based on that painting became available in Europe. Le Paon's painting is based on a Peale portrait, either a smaller Peale brought to France by the Marquis de Lafayette or one of the numerous prints after Peale's work. The portrait portrays Washington in the blue and buff Continental Army uniform, although the royal blue sash—seen in Peale's portrait—is gone and Washington's collar is depicted in a French style with a dark cravat. Le Paon also completed a portrait of Lafayette in his Continental Army uniform with his servant, James Armistead. The painting commemorated the victorious siege of Yorktown, seen in the background.

Detail of a letter from Lafayette to Washington, February 5, 1783, in which he proposes a plan to free slaves.

MARQUIS DE LAFAYETTE TO GEORGE WASHINGTON, FEBRUARY 5, 1783

Courtesy of David Bishop Skillman Library, Lafayette College
(MVLA, LC, N-YHS)

GEORGE WASHINGTON TO MARQUIS DE LAFAYETTE, APRIL 5, 1783

Courtesy of the Manuscripts Division, Library of Congress, Washington, D.C.
(MVLA)

In his letter, Lafayette effusively praised Washington and reminded him of their common bonds forged during the war. But one of Lafayette's central points regarded slavery. He wrote:

Permit me to Propose a plan to You Which Might Become Greatly Beneficial to the Black Part of Mankind. Let us Unite in Purchasing a Small Estate Where We May try the Experiment to free the Negroes, and Use them only as Tenants. Such an Exemple [sic] as Yours Might Render it a General Practice, and if We Succeed in America, I Will Chearfully [sic] Devote a part of My time to Render the Method fascionable [sic] in the West Indias [sic].[30]

Washington responded to Lafayette's anti-slavery proposal by stating he would be happy to join the Frenchman in such important work. Washington also noted he and Lafayette would discuss the details during their next visit.

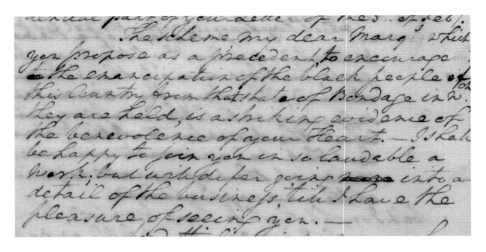

Detail of a letter from Washington to Lafayette, April 5, 1783, regarding slavery.

Washington later concluded the best way to eliminate slavery, without risking the still-tenuous union, was through gradual emancipation by state legislatures. However, in his last years he attempted to rent outlying Mount Vernon farms to immigrants who would hire his slaves. This plan, which may have been inspired in part by Lafayette's earlier proposal, was not successful, but Washington made the most famous manumission in American history when he made provisions to free his slaves in his will.

BROADSIDE INCLUDING A TESTIMONIAL FROM THE MARQUIS DE LAFAYETTE AND A PORTRAIT OF JAMES ARMISTEAD, 1824

John Blennerhassett Martin (1797-1857), American

Courtesy of David Bishop Skillman Library, Lafayette College
(MVLA, LC, N-YHS)

In 1781 James Armistead, an enslaved African American from near Williamsburg, Virginia, volunteered to enlist in nearby American forces serving under the Marquis de Lafayette. Helped by his knowledge of the area, Armistead spied on the British army and relayed important intelligence to the marquis. During the Yorktown campaign, Armistead is believed to have worked as a servant in the camp of British General Cornwallis, where he gathered additional information about the enemy. Cornwallis was reportedly surprised to see Armistead in Lafayette's camp at the end of the siege.

When Lafayette returned to Virginia in 1784, he recorded his gratitude for

This is to certify that the Bearer by the Name of James has done Essential Services to Me while I had the Honour to Command in this State. His Intelligence from the Enemy's Camp were Industriously Collected and more faithfully delivered. He perfectly Acquitted Himself with Some Important Commissions I gave him and Appears to me Entitled to every reward his Situation Can Admit of. Done under My Hand, Richmond November 21st 1786

Lafayette

James Armistead broadside.

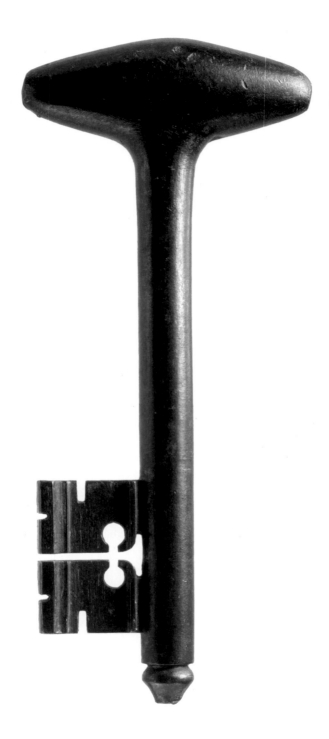

Key to the Bastille sent by Lafayette to Washington.

Armistead's "Essential Service" of gathering "Intelligence from the Ennemy's [sic] camp." Lafayette wrote: "He Perfectly Acquitted Himself With Some Important Commissions I Gave Him and Appears to me Entitled to Every Reward His Situation Can Admit of."[29]

Armistead's accomplishments and Lafayette's testimonial were influential in the Virginia legislature's decision to free Armistead in 1787 and later place him on the veterans' pension list. Armistead returned the tribute by taking the surname Lafayette.

James Blennerhasset Martin, an artist in Richmond, Virginia, created this broadside by uniting Lafayette's text with a portrait of Armistead he had painted earlier.

MARQUIS DE LAFAYETTE TO GEORGE WASHINGTON, MARCH 17, 1790

Courtesy of David Bishop Skillman Library, Lafayette College
(MVLA, LC, N-YHS)

KEY TO THE BASTILLE

France, Iron, ca. 1789

Transferred to the Mount Vernon Ladies' Association
through the generosity of John A. Washington III, 1860
(MVLA, LC, N-YHS)

SKETCH OF THE BASTILLE

Cathala, Pen, ink, and wash on paper, 1789

Courtesy of The Shriners Hospitals for Children and The Masonic Charity Foundation of Connecticut
(MVLA, LC, N-YHS)

In 1790 Lafayette reported to Washington on the current state of the French Revolution and sent his "Beloved General" two especially important gifts: "the Main Kea [sic]" of the Bastille and a drawing of that "fortress of despotism . . . just as it looked a few days after I

Sketch of the Bastille by Cathala, 1789, sent to Washington by Lafayette at the beginning of the French Revolution.

Had ordered its demolition."[31] He wrote: "It is a tribute Which I owe as A Son to My Adoptive father, as an aid de Camp to My General, As a Missionary of liberty to its patriarch."[32]

Thomas Paine carried these tributes to Washington at the executive residence in New York. Shortly before retiring from the presidency, Washington sent them to Mount Vernon. Washington acknowledged Lafayette's gifts, calling them a

> *token of victory gained by Liberty over Despotism. . . . In this great subject of great triumph for the new World, and for humanity in general, it will never be forgotten how conspicuous a part you bore, and how much luster you reflected on a country in which you made the first displays of character.[33]*

Washington hoped Lafayette, "the principal Pilot" of the "Ship" of the French Revolution, would guide it until it was "securely harboured in the haven of national tranquility, freedom, and glory, to which she is destined, and which I hope she is near attaining."[34]

SALVER

France, Silver plate, ca. 1783

The Mount Vernon Ladies' Association. Gift of Dr. and Mrs. John H. Gibbons, 1985
(MVLA, LC, N-YHS)

WINE COASTER

France, Silver plate, wood, ca. 1783

The Mount Vernon Ladies' Association. Purchase, 1981
Conservation courtesy of the Life Guard Society of Mount Vernon
(MVLA, LC, N-YHS)

George Washington, upon learning that silver-plated wares (French plate) were "fashionable and much used in genteel houses,"[35] wrote to Lafayette in October 1783 to request that he acquire as soon as possible an array of silver-plated tea wares and other tablewares, including "Two smaller size [salvers] for 6 wine glasses each" and "Eight Bottle sliders."[36] By December of 1783, Washington had moved to New York, where silver-plated wares were readily available. He wrote to Lafayette withdrawing his request, but Lafayette had already sent several items to satisfy Washington's wishes. By March 1784 Washington had received the items from France, including this salver (tray) and bottle slider (wine coaster). The tray is decorated with a simple beaded edge and engraved coat of arms; Washington had requested that "If this kind of plated Ware will bear engraving, I should be glad to have my arms thereon."[37] The wine coaster exhibits more intricate neoclassical design elements, with pierced and engraved swags and floral motifs. The Washingtons would have used these elegant pieces to entertain their many guests.

GOLDEN PHEASANTS

Native to China

Courtesy of the Ornithology Department, Museum of Comparative Zoology,
President and Fellows of Harvard College
(MVLA, LC, N-YHS)

In 1786 Lafayette sent to Mount Vernon three asses from Malta which George Washington had requested for use on his farm, two partridges, and seven pheasants. The pheasants had been given to Lafayette from the aviary of King Louis XVI, where the rare and beautiful birds had been imported and raised for several decades. Charles Willson Peale, artist and friend of Washington, heard of this unusual cargo and requested that Washington send him the pheasants, should they die, for his Philadelphia museum. In January 1787 Washington responded to Peale. "I cannot say that I shall be happy to have it in my power to comply with your request by sending you the bodies of my Pheasants; but I am afraid it will not be long before they will compose a part of your Museum, as they all appear to be drooping." Washington kept his word to send the pheasants as they "make their exit."[38] Preserving these two birds was among the earliest of Peale's forays into taxidermy, a process he would perfect over the coming years. Peale's museum, showing preserved examples from the natural world alongside portraits and sculptures of the world's great men, was a pioneering venture, which Washington supported through an annual subscription.

Additional artifacts in Section I include:

Leutze-Stellwagen Mask of Washington
Jean-Antoine Houdon (1741-1828), French
Plaster, 1785 or later

Courtesy of the Corcoran Gallery of Art, Washington, D.C.,
Gift of Edward J. Stellwagen
(MVLA)

Washington and Lafayette at the Battle of Brandywine
John Vanderlyn (1775-1852), American
Oil on canvas, ca. 1825

Courtesy of the Gilcrease Museum, Tulsa, Oklahoma
(MVLA)

Washington and His Generals at Yorktown
Charles Willson Peale (1741-1827), American
Oil on canvas, ca. 1784

Courtesy of the Maryland Historical Society,
Gift of Robert Gilmor, Jr.
(MVLA, N-YHS)

Marquis de Lafayette to Unknown Recipient, July 4, 1779

Courtesy of Mr. and Mrs. E. Kimbark MacColl, Portland, Oregon
(MVLA)

Marquis de Lafayette to George Washington, October 14, 1782

Courtesy of David Bishop Skillman Library, Lafayette College
(MVLA)

Marquis de Lafayette to George Washington, April 12, 1782

Courtesy of David Bishop Skillman Library, Lafayette College
(LC)

Marquis de Lafayette to George Washington, December 4, 1782

Courtesy of David Bishop Skillman Library, Lafayette College
(N-YHS)

Marquis de Lafayette to George Washington, July 8, 1781

The Gilder Lehrman Collection, courtesy of the Gilder Lehrman Institute of American History, NY
(MVLA)

Marquis de Lafayette to Samuel Cooper, October 26, 1781

The Gilder Lehrman Collection, courtesy of the Gilder Lehrman Institute of American History, NY
(MVLA, LC)

Marquis de Lafayette to James McHenry, November 22, 1801

The Gilder Lehrman Collection, courtesy of the Gilder Lehrman Institute of American History, NY
(N-YHS)

Marquis de Lafayette to Mr. Bayley, April 15, 1829

The Gilder Lehrman Collection, courtesy of the Gilder Lehrman Institute of American History, NY
(LC)

William Gordon to George Washington, Auguest 30, 1784

Courtesy of the Manuscripts Division, Library of Congress, Washington, D.C.
(N-YHS)

Act of Congress to pay the Marquis de Lafayette for his services during the American Revolution, December 2, 1793

Courtesy of David Bishop Skillman Library, Lafayette College
(MVLA, LC, N-YHS)

Gilbert du Motier, Marquis de Lafayette

Joseph Boze (1744-1825), French, Oil on canvas, ca. 1790

Courtesy of the Massachusetts Historical Society
(MVLA, N-YHS)

Lafayette's Sword

France, Steel, brass, ca. 1785-1790

Courtesy of David Bishop Skillman Library, Lafayette College
(MVLA, LC, N-YHS)

Marquis de Lafayette Medal

Rambert Dumarest (1760-1806), French, Bronze, 1789

Courtesy of the Society of the Cincinnati, Washington, D.C.,
The Robert Charles Lawrence Fergusson Collection
(MVLA, LC, N-YHS)

Marquis de Lafayette Medal

Rambert Dumarest (1760-1806), French, Bronze, 1789

Courtesy of David Bishop Skillman Library, Lafayette College
(MVLA, LC, N-YHS)

Marquis de Lafayette to George Washington, June 10, 1783

Courtesy of the Fondation Josée et René de Chambrun, Paris, France
(MVLA, LC, N-YHS)

Washington Family Portraits

James Sharples (1751/1752-1811)

American, Pastel on paper, 1796-1797

(MVLA)

George Washington (1732-1799)

The Mount Vernon Ladies' Association. Purchase, 1954

Martha Washington (1731-1802)

The Mount Vernon Ladies' Association. Purchase, 1954

George Washington Parke Custis (1781-1857)

Courtesy of Washington-Custis-Lee Collection,
Washington and Lee University, Lexington, Virginia

George Washington Lafayette (1779-1849)

The Mount Vernon Ladies' Association.
Gift of Mrs. A. Smith Bowman, Jr. and Mr. Robert E. Lee IV, 1985

Eleanor Parke Custis (1779-1852)

The Mount Vernon Ladies' Association. Purchase, 1974

George Washington to Benjamin Franklin, December 28, 1778

Courtesy of an anonymous lender
(MVLA)

Marquis de Lafayette to George Washington, December 31, 1777

Courtesy of David Bishop Skillman Library, Lafayette College
(MVLA)

Marquis de Lafayette to George Washington, July 22, 1783

Courtesy of David Bishop Skillman Library, Lafayette College
(MVLA)

Marquis de Lafayette to George Washington, November 11, 1783

Courtesy of David Bishop Skillman Library, Lafayette College
(MVLA)

Adrienne de Noailles de Lafayette to George Washington, April 17, 1785

Courtesy of The Arthur H. and Mary Marden Dean Lafayette Collection;
Cornell University Library, Ithaca, New York
(N-YHS)

George Washington to Marquis de Lafayette, October 8, 179[7] (Mistakenly Dated 1798 by Washington)

The Mount Vernon Ladies' Association. Gift of Mr. William K. Bixby, 1928
(MVLA)

Martha Washington to Marquis de Lafayette, October 31, 1800

Courtesy of the Fondation Josée et René de Chambrun, Paris, France
(MVLA, LC, N-YHS)

Leaf from Washington's Tomb

Leaf, ink, ca. 1799

Courtesy of the Fondation Josée et René de Chambrun, Paris, France
(MVLA, LC, N-YHS)

G. Washington in his Last Illness

Unidentified artist, Etching, 1800

The Mount Vernon Ladies' Association. Gift of Christine Meadows, 1993
(MVLA, LC, N-YHS)

Sèvres Tea Service

France
Porcelain, ca. 1780

The Mount Vernon Ladies' Association.
Gift of Dr. and Mrs. John H. Gibbons, 1985
(MVLA, LC, N-YHS)

Portrait Ring

Gold, probably 18th century

The Mount Vernon Ladies' Association.
Bequest of Ella Mackubin, 1956
(MVLA, LC, N-YHS)

SECTION II
The Nation's Guest
1824-1825

At the invitation of President James Monroe on behalf of the American people, Lafayette returned as "the Nation's Guest" on August 15, 1824. A welcome address given by the Mayor of New York City expressed the overall sentiment of the visit—"I bid you a sincere welcome to the shores of a country, of whose freedom and happiness you will ever be considered one of the most honored and beloved founders."[1] Lafayette's arrival in New York brought together an unprecedented number of American admirers—as many as 30,000 at his landing in Castle Garden and an additional 50,000 along the procession route to City Hall just a mile away.[2] It was the first of many exuberant celebrations. An observer of the Castle Garden festivities wrote:

> *It is impossible fully to describe the enthusiasm of joy which pervaded and was expressed by the whole multitude. Here the General had a fair specimen of the affection and respect, which is felt for him by every individual of this extended country. He seemed much moved by these expressions of attachment, and bowed continually to the people who pressed about him.[3]*

Although he initially planned to travel only to the original thirteen states, Lafayette extended his tour to thirteen months and stopped in major cities and small towns in all twenty-four states. Record-breaking crowds gathered to pay tribute at every stop. He visited sites of memorable Revolutionary War battles. These included Yorktown, where he and others celebrated the anniversary of that great victory and a soldier urged him to remain in the United States to be buried at his death alongside Washington. In 1825 Lafayette attended the laying of the cornerstone at the Bunker Hill monument.

Lafayette was accompanied on the lengthy tour by his son—and General Washington's namesake—George Washington Lafayette, who served as a tangible reminder of the close friendship between the two heroes of the American Revolution. Lafayette's secretary, Auguste Levasseur, and valet, Bastien, completed the party. Their coach travel often involved inhospitable terrain, bad weather, and rough roads. They attempted to stay on schedule for events, even if that meant continuing through the night. Travel by boat was

The Tour of Gen. Lafayette, 1824. David Bishop Skillman Library, Lafayette College.

somewhat less treacherous, although at least two serious steamboat accidents occurred during Lafayette's journey. One steamboat which carried the party was shipwrecked in thick fog on the Hudson River, and another named *Mechanic* went aground while traveling on the Ohio River in Illinois. Most of Lafayette's luggage was lost on the *Mechanic*, and he slept the remainder of the night on the shore on a mattress retrieved from the wreckage.[4] At age sixty-seven, Lafayette bore it all with seemingly little discomfort, aided undoubtedly by immeasurable feelings of pride at the honors bestowed on him at every turn.

In Lafayette, Americans saw a living link to George Washington and the glories of the founding era. Local governments, civic organizations, groups affiliated with those who fought in the American Revolution (such as the Society of the Cincinnati), and Masonic lodges fêted him with parades, public orations, private dinners, and gala balls. At Lafayette's request, his hosts at the multitude of events in his honor introduced him as an American general. Lafayette received numerous tributes and accolades, including more honorary degrees from Masonic lodges than had ever been bestowed on one man. In

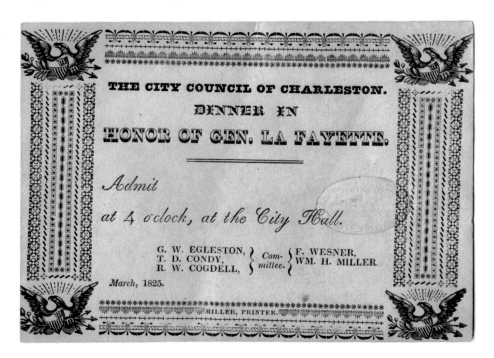

Admission card from the City Council of Charleston Dinner, 1825. David Bishop Skillman Library, Lafayette College.

response to the ceremony at the Washington Lodge in Alexandria given in his honor, Lafayette responded:

I receive with peculiar sensation, this mark of kindness and attention, and these expressions of esteem from my Masonic Brethren, and it is particularly gratifying to my feelings to visit a Lodge over which our lamented illustrious Brother Washington presided. I shall ever cherish a high regard for Masonry, and pray you, Worshipful Sir, and the rest of the Brethren, to accept my particular and grateful acknowledgements.[5]

In December 1824 Lafayette addressed both houses of Congress, the first foreign dignitary to do so. There were formal gatherings arranged by established organizations, but also informal public gatherings where people could meet, or at least catch a glimpse of, the French hero. Slaves, free blacks, and American Indians were generally barred from attending these events, but the abolitionist Lafayette met with members of those groups on a few occasions when the opportunity presented itself.

Lafayette's tour spawned many commemorative objects made for sale as souvenirs. Ceramic pitchers, plates, glassware, fabric banners, and ribbons were among those keepsakes that depicted Washington and Lafayette together. Dutch artist Ary Scheffer's painting of Lafayette, as well as images from prints and engravings, were replicated frequently on commemorative objects of the period.

During the trip, Lafayette and his son reconnected with their American family—the Washingtons. They visited Mount Vernon to mourn at Washington's tomb and to embrace the descendants of George and Martha Washington. George Washington Lafayette, who had spent more than two years of his youth with the Washington family to escape prison and the guillotine during the French Revolution, was welcomed as kin by the family's younger generations. In an 1824 letter to George Washington Parke Custis, young Lafayette wrote, "Good night my dear Custis—receive the expression of my brotherly friendship."[6] An account of Lafayette's visit to Custis' Arlington House described Lafayette's departure following a brief evening engagement:

. . . the General came out & seemed astonished at the surrounding throng, for now, not only the party and the torch-bearers were under the portico, but the people of the place collected on the steps of the Temple while the ladies wav'd their white handkerchiefs in token of respect & honor for one who deserved their smiles &

admiration—of all the spectacles this was the most fairy-like which has yet been witnessed since the arrival of the nation's guest—the friend of Washington . . . the light placing, as it were, our nations benefactor in a resplendent halo of glory.[7]

On September 6, 1825, Lafayette attended a state dinner at the White House, and Arlington House was illuminated in honor of his birthday. The following day, a farewell ceremony with President James Monroe brought the triumphal tour to a close. With a military escort, Lafayette embarked on the steamboat *Mount Vernon*, waving his farewell to Washington's home as he came down the Potomac River. On September 9 he was received on the frigate *Brandywine* which would carry him back to France. Recognizing this as likely his final trip across the Atlantic, Lafayette carried with him a trunk of American soil from Bunker Hill for his grave.

Pair of porcelain Marquis de Lafayette urn-shaped vases, French, ca. 1824-1830. Diplomatic Reception Rooms, United States Department of State.

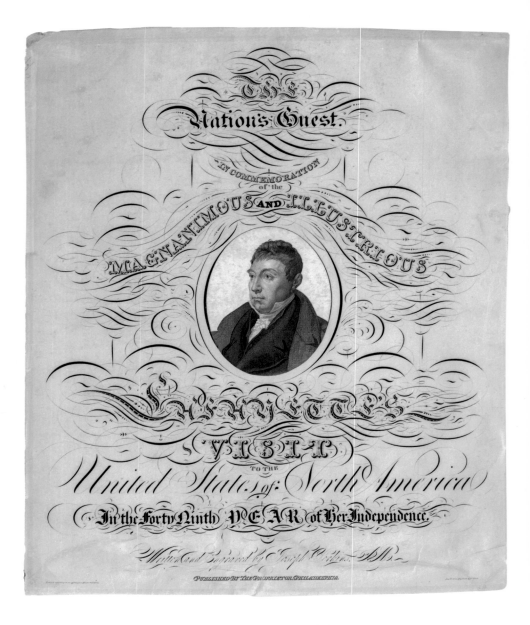

Calligraphic tribute to Lafayette by Joseph Perkins, ca 1825.

Marquis de Lafayette

Jean-Marie Leroux (1788-1870), French, after Ary Scheffer (1795-1858), Dutch
Engraving, 1824

Courtesy of David Bishop Skillman Library, Lafayette College
(MVLA, LC, N-YHS)

The Nation's Guest, in Commemoration of the Magnanimous and Illustrious Lafayette's Visit to the United States of North America in the Forty-Ninth Year of Her Independence

Joseph Perkins (1788-1842), American
Engraving, ca. 1825

Courtesy of David Bishop Skillman Library, Lafayette College
(MVLA, LC, N-YHS)

Lafayette's fame during his triumphant tour as "the Nation's Guest" spurred the creation of many mementos or souvenirs, including this 1824 engraving of the Frenchman. Leroux based his print on an 1823 painting by Ary Scheffer, reportedly Lafayette's favorite portrait of himself, depicting the Frenchman in elegant yet understated attire reflecting his status as a republican. This large portrait now hangs in the Chamber of the United States House of Representatives. In 1834, Congress commissioned a portrait of Washington as a companion; it hangs on the opposite side of the rostrum.

Lafayette carried many copies of this engraving to America and distributed the prints to friends. It quickly became the preeminent image of Lafayette during this era.

Because of the widespread appeal and marketability of this engraving, many enterprising engravers and craftsmen used it as the basis for their own prints and souvenirs. Joseph Perkins used the Leroux image in his elaborate calligraphic tribute to the marquis.

Portrait of Lafayette completed by Sully in 1833.

Portrait of Lafayette

Thomas Sully (1783-1872), American
Oil on canvas, 1826-1833

Courtesy of Lafayette College Art Collection, 1987
(MVLA, LC, N-YHS)

On September 1, 1824, the Philadelphia City Council commissioned Thomas Sully to paint the city's coat of arms for the triumphal arch being erected in preparation for Lafayette's visit.[8] Sully, having by that time established himself as one of the city's foremost portrait painters, also provided a portrait of William Penn that month for a room in Independence Hall which was being "fitted up for Lafayette."[9] On October 2, a committee named The Citizens of Philadelphia sent a letter to Lafayette stating that "A number of our most respectable citizens are desirous of presenting to the city of Philadelphia your portrait by Sully, should you consent to sit for it."[10] Lafayette did consent. An autobiography Sully wrote years later indicates that in December 1824 "Lafayette I painted from life in Washington."[11] This likely refers to an ink and watercolor sketch which was completed around that time.

It is unclear whether Lafayette sat for Sully again during the 1824-1825 tour. Nonetheless, according to Sully's register, this small study for the large Philadelphia commission was begun on January 16, 1826 but then "put by" and not completed until 1833.[12] Sully had gained a reputation for painting flattering portraits, and this image of Lafayette is no exception. The aging Frenchman's wrinkles have been smoothed out, his toupée looks natural, and his stance portrays a vigorous hero. The parade welcoming Lafayette to Philadelphia is depicted in the background.

PRESENTED

to

Gen.ˡ LaFayette,

BY

A. Denmead	F. B. Booth
W. Smith	E. Duffy
I. M. Miller	I. P. Redding
W.ᵐ H. Miller	O. C. Osborne
M. H. Keene	R. E. France
G. Dunan	A. W.ᵐ Barnes
I. A. Roche	W.ᵐ S. Branson

In behalf of the YOUNG MEN,

OF

BALTIMORE.

October 1824

C. Pryce Pox.t   J. Sands Sc.

LAFAYETTE MEDALLION

Charles Pryce (silversmith, active ca.
1824-1834), probably engraved by
John Sands, both Baltimore
Gold, ca. 1824

*Courtesy of the Collection of the Museum of Early
Southern Decorative Arts,
Winston-Salem, North Carolina
(MVLA, LC, N-YHS)*

On April 18, 1781, Lafayette
wrote to General Washington: "The
merchants of Baltimore lent me a
sum of about 2,000 pounds, which
will procure some shirts, linen,
overalls, shoes, and a few hats. The
ladies will make up the shirts, and the
overalls will be made by the
detachment, so that our soldiers have
a chance of being a little more

*Above, Lafayette Medallion, front. At left, view of
the reverse.*

comfortable."[13] The citizens of Baltimore, having assisted Lafayette and his
troops during the Revolutionary War, developed an affectionate bond with
them.

The American and Commercial Daily Advertiser published a notice on
September 21, 1824, encouraging young men of Baltimore—ranging in age
from seventeen to twenty-one—to attend a meeting for the commission of a
medal that would be presented to Lafayette during his upcoming visit to the
city. None of the fourteen who commissioned the piece (and whose names are
engraved on the reverse) was born until after the American Revolution had
concluded and Lafayette had returned to France. Clearly, Baltimore's fondness
for Lafayette had been passed down to the next generation. The symbolism in
the decoration of this piece is emblematic of the resurgence in patriotic fervor
surrounding Lafayette's triumphal tour and specifically commemorates the
victory at Yorktown. Lafayette wore this medallion on a sash for the duration
of his 1824 visit to Baltimore, taking it with him when he returned to France.
It is considered one of the finest examples of early American goldsmithing.

PLATTER

James & Ralph Clews (active ca. 1818-1836), English, after Samuel Maverick (1789-1845), American
Porcelain, ca. 1825-1830

Commemorative ceramics, often common tablewares such as platters, plates, teapots and pitchers, were abundant during Lafayette's tour. From 1819 to 1834, the Staffordshire ceramic manufactory of J & R Clews made transfer-printed wares in a variety of colors, with blue being the most predominant. Many of the designs by brothers James and Ralph Clews were based on popular prints of the time. That is the case with this platter, part of a dinner service, depicting the scene of Lafayette's 1824 arrival at Castle Garden in New York, where 30,000 Americans gathered to welcome him. The image derives from the most recognizable and commonly recreated image of Lafayette's tour by American engraver Samuel Maverick. Lafayette's ship *Cadmus* is escorted to Castle Garden by eight additional ships, with the American flag bearing twenty-four stars flapping in the wind, and the smoke of a cannon salute from Fort Lafayette in New York Harbor billowing in the air. The August 17 issue of the *Commercial Advertiser* reported: "The view of this fleet will perhaps never be forgotten. It was not only unique, but beyond a doubt one of the most splendid spectacles ever witnessed on this part of the globe."[14]

MASONIC APRON

Probably America
Silk, ca. 1825

Courtesy of the Society of the Cincinnati, Washington, D.C., Gift of Isabel Anderson, 1938
(MVLA, LC, N-YHS)

The Masonic brotherhood was an important bond between George Washington and the Marquis de Lafayette. Both men joined the fraternal order at an early age. Washington received his first degree from the Fredericksburg, Virginia, Lodge in November 1752 at the age of twenty. Lafayette is believed to have joined by 1775 in conjunction with one of his French military regiments. Not surprisingly, Masonic lodges in every corner of the United States felt a special connection to Lafayette, whom they lavishly celebrated on his American tour. This Royal Arch apron is thought to have been worn by Lafayette at the Washington Lodge in Alexandria for just such an occasion in 1825. The Master of the lodge, Brother Thomas Simms, began his remarks to the gathering by stating:

> *Illustrious Brother Lafayette: Among the various demonstrations of joy which your arrival in the United States has elicited from the hearts of its grateful citizens, none have been more truly respectful or more sincerely tendered, than the cordial welcome of your Masonic Brethren.*[15]

LE GÉNÉRAL LAFAYETTE.

LAFAYETTE'S DREAM ON THE DECK OF THE BRANDYWINE

Achille Moreau (ca. 1800-ca. 1845) after Jean Auguste Dubouloz (1800-1870), both French
Etching and aquatint, 1825

Courtesy of David Bishop Skillman Library, Lafayette College
(MVLA, LC, N-YHS)

Lafayette made two pilgrimages to Mount Vernon—one near the beginning and one near the end of his triumphal tour. On August 29 and 30, 1825 he visited the home and burial site of his beloved general one last time. Shortly after a state dinner at the White House hosted by President John Quincy

Adams in September, Lafayette left the city of Washington on the steamship *Mount Vernon*. A local newspaper reported that he waved farewell to Washington's home as the ship passed.[16] Lafayette soon boarded the frigate *Brandywine*, named for the Revolutionary War battle in which he had been wounded, for his return to France.

This allegorical print depicts Lafayette onboard the *Brandywine* with "the spirits of the defenders of the *Américain* liberty" visiting him during his passage. Washington and Benjamin Franklin are clearly recognizable, as is the personification of America in the form of an Indian kneeling on the deck. The legend identifies the figures at the upper left corner of the print as "the genii protectors of America [who] drive away the storms" during Lafayette's voyage.

ADDITIONAL ARTIFACTS IN SECTION II INCLUDE:

LAFAYETTE'S COPY OF THE DECLARATION OF INDEPENDENCE, PUBLISHED BY WILLIAM J. STONE; WASHINGTON, D.C., 1823

Courtesy of the Albert H. Small Declaration of Independence Collection, Special Collections, University of Virginia Library, Charlottesville, Va.
(MVLA, LC, N-YHS)

BLOCK-PRINTED BANNER

W. Farrow, American
Cotton, ca. 1824

Courtesy of David Bishop Skillman Library, Lafayette College
(MVLA, LC, N-YHS)

HAIL! LA FAYETTE!

Written by Major J. N. Barker and adapted to Gen'l. La Fayette's March
Sheet music, 1824

Courtesy of David Bishop Skillman Library, Lafayette College
(MVLA, LC, N-YHS)

ORDER OF RECEPTION FOR THE MARQUIS DE LAFAYETTE; LOUISVILLE, KENTUCKY, 1825

Courtesy of David Bishop Skillman Library, Lafayette College
(MVLA, LC, N-YHS)

COMMEMORATIVE DRUM

Abner Stevens, American
Wood, leather, brass tacks, ca. 1824

Courtesy of the Collection of Old Sturbridge Village
(MVLA, LC, N-YHS)

FLASK

Kensington Glass Works, Philadelphia
Aquamarine glass, cork, ca. 1824-1825

Courtesy of David Bishop Skillman Library, Lafayette College
(MVLA, LC, N-YHS)

FLASK

Kensington Glass Works, Philadelphia
Aquamarine glass, ca. 1824-1825

Courtesy of David Bishop Skillman Library, Lafayette College
(MVLA, LC, N-YHS)

FLASK

Thomas Stebbins, Coventry, Connecticut
Olive amber glass, ca. 1824-1825

Courtesy of David Bishop Skillman Library, Lafayette College
(MVLA, LC, N-YHS)

FLASK

Stebbins and Stebbins, Coventry, Connecticut
Olive amber glass, ca. 1824-1825

Courtesy of David Bishop Skillman Library, Lafayette College
(MVLA, LC, N-YHS)

FLASK

Thomas Stebbins and Chamberlain, Coventry, Connecticut
Olive amber glass, ca. 1824-1825

Courtesy of David Bishop Skillman Library, Lafayette College
(MVLA, LC, N-YHS)

VASES

France, possibly Paris
Porcelain with overglaze enamels and gilt, ca. 1824-1830

Courtesy of the Diplomatic Reception Rooms,
U.S. Department of State, Washington, DC
(MVLA, LC, N-YHS)

VEILLEUSE

France, possibly Paris
Porcelain with overglaze enamels and gilt, ca. 1824

Courtesy of the Kiplinger family
(MVLA, LC, N-YHS)

PLATE

Probably made by Smith Pottery of Norwalk, Connecticut
Earthenware, ca. 1824-1825

Courtesy of David Bishop Skillman Library, Lafayette College
(MVLA, LC, N-YHS)

TEACUP

Earthenware, ca. 1824-1825

The Mount Vernon Ladies' Association.
Gift of Mrs. Randall H. Hagner, Jr., Vice Regent for the District of Columbia, 1986
(MVLA, LC, N-YHS)

PITCHER

Richard Hall and Sons, Staffordshire, England
Earthenware, ca. 1825-1830

The Mount Vernon Ladies' Association.
Gift of Mrs. Clare C. Edwards, Vice Regent for Connecticut, 2001
(MVLA, LC, N-YHS)

PITCHER

Richard Hall and Sons, Staffordshire, England
Earthenware, ca. 1825-1830

Courtesy of David Bishop Skillman Library, Lafayette College
(MVLA, LC, N-YHS)

PITCHER

Richard Hall and Sons, Staffordshire, England
Earthenware, ca. 1825-1830

Courtesy of David Bishop Skillman Library, Lafayette College
(MVLA, LC, N-YHS)

PITCHER

Richard Hall and Sons, Staffordshire, England
Earthenware, ca. 1825-1830

Courtesy of David Bishop Skillman Library, Lafayette College
(MVLA, LC, N-YHS)

PUNCH BOWL

Probably England or France
Porcelain, after 1830

Courtesy of the New-York Historical Society
(N-YHS)

MARQUIS DE LAFAYETTE

Villain, after Antoine Maurin (1793-1860), French
Lithograph, ca. 1824–1834

Courtesy of David Bishop Skillman Library, Lafayette College
(MVLA, LC, N-YHS)

RIBBON

Richmond, Virginia
Silk, ca. 1824

Courtesy of David Bishop Skillman Library, Lafayette College,
(MVLA, LC, N-YHS)

RIBBON

America
Silk, ca. 1824

Courtesy of David Bishop Skillman Library, Lafayette College
(MVLA, LC, N-YHS)

RIBBON

H. Korn (retailer), Philadelphia
Silk, ca. 1824

Courtesy of David Bishop Skillman Library, Lafayette College
(MVLA, LC, N-YHS)

RIBBON

H. Korn (retailer), Philadelphia
Silk, ca. 1824

Courtesy of David Bishop Skillman Library, Lafayette College
(MVLA, LC, N-YHS)

MOSES W. JORDAN TO RUTH SMITH, OCTOBER 10, 1824

The Gilder Lehrman Collection,
Courtesy of the Gilder Lehrman Institute of American History, NY
(MVLA)

Daveis-Lafayette Society of the Cincinnati Eagle

Paris, France, after a 1783 insignia by Pierre L'Enfant
Gold, 1832

Courtesy of the Society of the Cincinnati, Washington, D.C.,
Bequest of Mabel S. Daveis, 1950
(MVLA, LC, N-YHS)

Medal Honoring Lafayette

François-Augustin Caunois, French
Bronze, 1824

The Mount Vernon Ladies' Association.
Gift of Mr. & Mrs. Lyttleton B.P. Gould, Jr., M. Chapin Krech, Shepard Krech, M.D.,
Alvin W. Krech, Peter Chapin and Charles Chapin
in memory of Esther Maria Lewis Chapin, 1983
(MVLA, LC, N-YHS)

Playing Card Featuring the Marquis de Lafayette as the Ace of Spades

Jazaniah Ford, Massachusetts
Engraving, 1824

Courtesy of David Bishop Skillman Library, Lafayette College
(MVLA, LC, N-YHS)

An Acrostic on the General whom Ten Millions of People Delight to Honor

Philadelphia, 1824

Courtesy of David Bishop Skillman Library, Lafayette College
(MVLA, LC, N-YHS)

Martha Washington's Recipe for "The Finest Lip Salve in the World"

Copied by Eleanor Parke Custis Lewis for Lafayette's grandchildren
December 17, 1824

Courtesy of The Arthur H. and Mary Marden Dean Lafayette Collection;
Cornell University Library, Ithaca, New York
(MVLA)

Eleanor Parke Custis Lewis to Elizabeth Bordley Gibson, November 24, 1824

The Mount Vernon Ladies' Association. Purchase, 1951
(MVLA, LC)

Eleanor Parke Custis Lewis to Elizabeth Bordley Gibson, December 10, 1825

The Mount Vernon Ladies' Association. Purchase, 1952
(N-YHS)

Brooch

America
Gold, hair, crystal, ca. 1825

Courtesy of the Historical Society of Pennsylvania Collection,
Atwater Kent Museum of Philadelphia
(MVLA, LC, N-YHS)

Presentation Medal

Marquand & Brothers (active ca. 1830-1833), New York
Gold, 1832

Courtesy of the Winterthur Museum. Museum Purchase, 1978
(MVLA, LC, N-YHS)

Teacup and Saucer

England
Porcelain, ca. 1825

The Mount Vernon Ladies' Association. Purchased by the Barnes Fund, 2004
(MVLA, LC, N-YHS)

Invitation to a Fête for the Marquis de Lafayette at New York's Castle Garden, 1824

Courtesy of David Bishop Skillman Library, Lafayette College
(MVLA, LC, N-YHS)

The Tour of Gen. La Fayette, 1824

Courtesy of David Bishop Skillman Library, Lafayette College
(MVLA, LC, N-YHS)

Tumbler

America
Colorless glass, ca. 1790-1825

Courtesy of the Society of the Cincinnati, Washington, D.C.,
Gift of Dr. DuBose Egleston, Society of the Cincinnati of the State of South Carolina, 1960
(MVLA, LC, N-YHS)

Admission Card for the City Council of Charleston Dinner, 1825

Courtesy of David Bishop Skillman Library, Lafayette College
(MVLA, LC, N-YHS)

Itinerary of the Marquis de Lafayette, Likely in the Hand of George Washington Lafayette, April 15-16 [1824-1825]

The Mount Vernon Ladies' Association. On deposit by Mrs. Lawrence Lewis Conrad
(MVLA)

Address of the Citizens of Boston, ca. 1824

Courtesy of The Arthur H. and Mary Marden Dean Lafayette Collection;
Cornell University Library, Ithaca, New York
(MVLA)

Mayor of New York's Remarks to Lafayette

Courtesy of The Arthur H. and Mary Marden Dean Lafayette Collection;
Cornell University Library, Ithaca, New York
(N-YHS)

Scarf

America
Silk, ca. 1824

Courtesy of David Bishop Skillman Library, Lafayette College
(MVLA, LC, N-YHS)

Waistcoast

Cotton, silk, ca. 1824-1825

Courtesy of David Bishop Skillman Library, Lafayette College
(MVLA, LC, N-YHS)

Address to the Marquis de Lafayette from the Society of the Cincinnati of the State of Massachusetts, ca. 1824

Courtesy of The Arthur H. and Mary Marden Dean Lafayette Collection;
Cornell University Library, Ithaca, New York
(MVLA)

Diagram and Order of Procession in Honor of General Lafayette's Arrival in Delaware, September 11, 1824

Courtesy of the New-York Historical Society
(N-YHS)

Lady's Gloves

America
Kid leather, ca. 1824-1825

Courtesy of David Bishop Skillman Library, Lafayette College
(MVLA, LC, N-YHS)

*"Welcome Lafayette" drum made
by Abner Stevens, ca. 1824.
Old Sturbridge Village, 1.105.13.*

Gentleman's Gloves

America
Kid leather, ca. 1824-1825

*Courtesy of David Bishop Skillman Library
Lafayette College
(MVLA, LC, N-YHS)*

Jewelry Suite

England
Steel, ca. 1820

*Courtesy of the New-York Historical Society, New
York, Museum purchase
(MVLA, LC, N-YHS)*

Ball Gown

America
Silk satin and crepe, 1824

*Courtesy of The Valentine Richmond History Center
(MVLA)*

Playing card featuring the Marquis de Lafayette as the ace of spades by Jazaniah Ford, 1824. David Bishop Skillman Library, Lafayette College.

Their Fame Will Live Forever
1834 and the Enduring Legacy of Washington and Lafayette

Fewer than ten years after his triumphal tour as "the Nation's Guest," Lafayette died on May 20, 1834, in Paris, four months before his seventy-seventh birthday. His son, George Washington Lafayette, fulfilled his father's wish to be buried in both French and American soil by scattering around the coffin soil from Bunker Hill brought back for this purpose by his father. An American flag has flown over his grave since his burial.

When news of Lafayette's death reached America, it spurred a national outpouring of emotion. His death was a noteworthy event in itself, but it also signified the passing of the Revolutionary War generation in America. This living link to Washington and to other Founding Fathers was gone.

As President Andrew Jackson directed, Lafayette received the same military funeral honors that President John Adams had ordered for George Washington. These observances included flags flying at half-mast and cannon salutes in memory of the fallen hero. The United States Congress passed a joint resolution to convey its sorrow to Lafayette's family, draped its chambers in black bunting, and asked all Americans to dress in mourning for thirty days. Many of the groups that had honored Lafayette with speeches and receptions during his 1824-1825 tour sent their condolences to George Washington Lafayette and his family.

Former president John Quincy Adams, then serving in Congress as a representative from Massachusetts, gave the nation's official eulogy on December 31, 1834, during a joint session of Congress attended by President Jackson, his cabinet, the U.S. Supreme Court, and the diplomatic corps. Adams' remarks were similar to many of those made upon Washington's death by Henry Lee and other eulogists; both Lafayette and Washington were remembered as brave military commanders in pursuit of freedom and as paragons of the moral power of virtue.

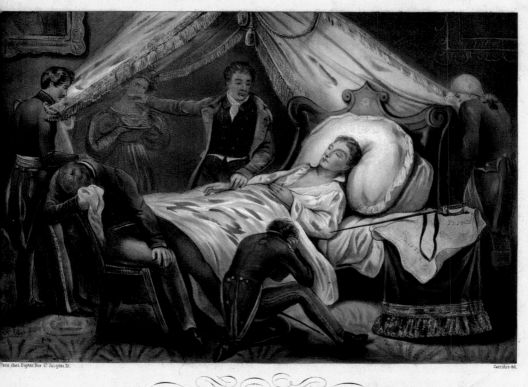

MORT DE LA FAYETTE.

Il n'est plus ce guerrier, qui héros des deux Mondes,   Que dis-je! il vit encore dans nos cœurs attendris;
Fonda la liberté sur des bases fécondes!!!....   La Fayette et le Peuple à jamais sont unis!!

Mort du General Lafayette *(The Death of General Lafayette), hand-colored woodcut, French,*
1834. David Bishop Skillman Library, Lafayette College.

When concluding his remarks on Lafayette's role in the Revolutionary War,
Adams wrote:

> *Where, in the rolls of History, where, in the fictions of Romance, where, but in the*
> *life of Lafayette, has been seen the noble stranger, flying, with the tribute of his name,*
> *his rank, his affluence, his ease, his domestic bliss, his treasure, his blood, to the relief*
> *of a suffering and distant land, in the hour of her deepest calamity—baring his*
> *bosom to her foes; and not at the transient pageantry of a tournament, but for a*
> *succession of five years sharing all the vicissitudes of her fortunes; always eager to*
> *appear at the post of danger. . . ?* [1]

Americans continued to celebrate Washington, Lafayette, and their shared
accomplishments—on occasions such as the centennials of the Battles of
Bunker Hill and Yorktown—with the creation of sculptures, medals, ribbons,
memorial prints, and other items. These images, often depicting both

Washington and Lafayette, emphasize the longstanding historical connections between the United States and France.

Images of Lafayette had a renewed popularity during World War I, when American forces helped liberate France. Lieutenant Colonel Charles E. Stanton, General John J. Pershing's aide, visited Lafayette's grave on the Fourth of July, 1917, proclaiming: "Lafayette, we are here!" Similar emotions echoed in music of that time; in 1917 Fred B. Teeling wrote "We'll Pay Our Debt to Lafayette." Almost twenty years later, on the 1934 centennial of Lafayette's death, President Franklin D. Roosevelt noted he cherished the marquis' memory "above that of any citizen of a foreign country."[2]

The United States Congress made "the Hero of Two Worlds" an honorary citizen in 2002. Only five other people have received this honor. Virginia Senator John Warner, author of this joint resolution, referred to Lafayette's success during the American Revolution and following years: "His tireless efforts, both as a liaison [to influential French policy makers] and as a general, aided America in her ultimate victory."[3]

APOTHÉOSE DE LAFAYETTE (APOTHEOSIS OF LAFAYETTE)

Unidentified artist
Etching and engraving, ca. 1834

Courtesy of David Bishop Skillman Library, Lafayette College
(MVLA, LC, N-YHS)

Washington and Lafayette were so closely associated in the minds of Americans that, in Washington's tent during the forty-third anniversary of the victory at Yorktown, Colonel William J. Lewis, a Virginia officer from the Revolutionary War, begged Lafayette not to leave America. Lewis instead implored him to be buried in what was often considered the sacred ground of Mount Vernon:

> *stay with us . . . and when it shall please the God of universal nature to call you to himself, crowned with the blessings of at least one free and mighty nation, we will then with holy devotion bury your bones by the side of your adopted and immortal Father and moisten your tomb with the tears of love and gratitude.*[4]

Although Lafayette did not heed the plea, many believed that he and Washington would be reunited eventually.

In this print, Generals Washington and Lafayette, who fought side by side

Washington welcomes Lafayette to heaven.

for liberty and regarded one another as surrogate father and son, share a poignant moment as Washington welcomes his friend to heaven, or as the print's text reads, "the temple of eternal fame." The marquis is escorted by an angel and by French soldiers.

An American Indian, representing the United States, kneels before both heroes, while a French soldier from the American Revolution greets Lafayette by removing his hat.[5] The French flag, which Lafayette helped design, features the date 1789, the beginning of the French Revolution.

Following their deaths, Washington and Lafayette appeared individually in a number of apotheosis prints that vividly communicate their godlike status and the enduring importance of their character and accomplishments.

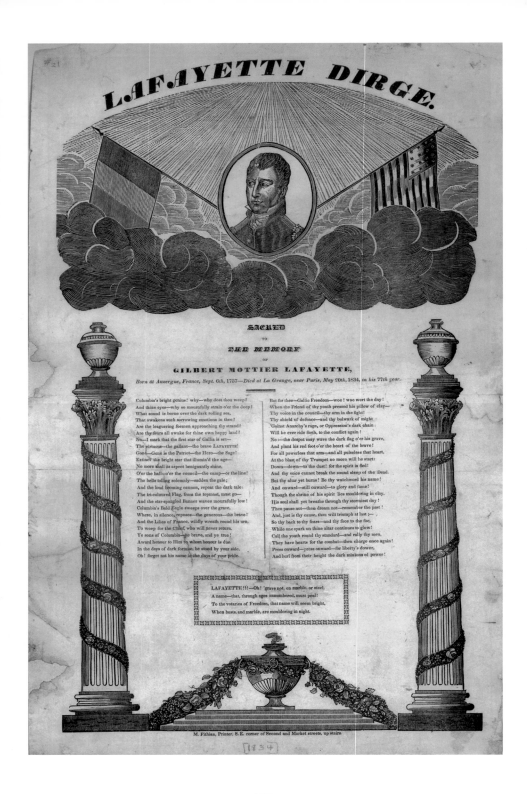

LAFAYETTE DIRGE

Broadside, M. Fithian (printer), Philadelphia, 1834

Courtesy of David Bishop Skillman Library, Lafayette College
(MVLA, LC, N-YHS)

Lafayette, now ascended to immortality, is surrounded by French and American flags, celestial clouds, and divine rays of blessing. The text refers to Columbia, a symbol of America, weeping while a bald eagle sweeps over Lafayette's grave, "Where, in silence, reposes—the generous, the brave!" Lafayette's service to freedom both in the United States and France is vividly detailed and eulogized; one verse refers to both countries' flags lowered in mourning. The left column of text, focusing mainly on Lafayette's success in the American Revolution, concludes with:

> *Ye sons of Columbia—ye brave and ye true!*
> *Award honour to Him to whom honour is due.*
> *In the days of dark fortune, he stood by your side,*
> *Oh! forget not his name in the days of your pride.*

Text appearing just above the memorial incense burner gives a last tribute to the fame and immortality Lafayette deserves:

> *LAFAYETTE!!!—Oh! 'grave not, on marble, or steel,*
> *A name—that, through ages unnumbered, must peal!*
> *To the votaries of Freedom, that name will seem bright*
> *When busts, and marble, are mouldering in night.*

At left, a dirge written the year of Lafayette's death.

SCARF

France
Silk, ca. 1917

Courtesy of the Society of the Cincinnati, Washington, D.C.,
Gift of Jacques Querenet, Société des Cincinnati de France, 1978
(MVLA, LC, N-YHS)

This silk-screened example is one of many commemorative scarves made to celebrate the arrival of American troops in France in 1917 and the subsequent Allied victory during World War I. The United States remained neutral until a series of events—including the sinking of the *Lusitania* and the

interception of a telegram in which Germany promised United States territory to Mexico in exchange for support—convinced President Woodrow Wilson to ask Congress for a formal declaration of war on April 2, 1917. These scarves were made and sold in France, often to American soldiers stationed there. The brightly colored pattern of this scarf depicts the flags of each of the Allied countries, as well as likenesses of President Wilson, George Washington, the Marquis de Lafayette, and

Scarf celebrating the Allied victory in World War I, with the phrase Gloire Aux Americains.

the Statue of Liberty, a gift from France to the United States. This combination of images reinforced the strong Franco-American alliance dating back to the American Revolution, in which Americans and French—symbolized by Washington and Lafayette—fought side by side for the cause of liberty. At the conclusion of World War I in 1918, Wilson became the first U.S. president to travel abroad while in office when he sailed to France to attend the Versailles Peace Conference aboard the *S.S. George Washington.*

PLATES

A.G. Richardson and Company, Limited,
trademarked as Crown Ducal (since 1916) England
Porcelain, ca. 1932

Green plate: The Mount Vernon Ladies' Association.
Gift of Mr. and Mrs. Gilbert L. Southworth, 1987
Other plates: Courtesy of Clare C. Edwards,
Mount Vernon Ladies' Association Vice Regent for Connecticut
(MVLA, LC, N-YHS)

THE HOME OF WASHINGTON

Thomas Oldham Barlow (1824-1889), English, after Thomas Pritchard Rossiter
(1818-1871) and Louis Rémy Mignot (1831-1870), both American
Publisher unknown
Engraving, 1860

Mount Vernon Ladies' Association. The Willard-Budd Collection,
Gift of Mr. and Mrs. Robert B. Gibby, 1984
(MVLA, LC, N-YHS)

In the mid-nineteenth century the publication of several biographies of
Washington, together with the preservation efforts of Ann Pamela
Cunningham and the Mount Vernon Ladies' Association, focused renewed
attention on Washington as a private citizen. Many artists, including Thomas
Rossiter and Louis Mignot, were inspired to paint scenes from Washington's
life. Rossiter, who visited Mount Vernon and made sketches there, wrote an
essay to accompany the exhibition of his and Mignot's monumental painting
depicting Washington, his family, and Lafayette on
the piazza at Mount Vernon in 1784. Rossiter
wrote "What thoughts of a Hero's repose are
awakened at mention of the beloved Home of the
venerated and idolized Father of the Nation!
What a Mecca of the Western Hemisphere is its
site!"[6]

Washington had invited Lafayette to visit, and,
after arriving at Mount Vernon, Lafayette wrote to
his wife: "I am reveling in the happiness of
finding my dear general again; . . . our meeting was
very tender and our satisfaction completely

*Detail of the reverse of Crown
Ducal plate.*

Washington and Lafayette
at Mount Vernon

Washington and Lafayette
at Mount Vernon.

...ton and Lafayette
... Mount Vernon

This 19th-century print depicts Lafayette's 1784 visit to the Washingtons at Mount Vernon.

mutual."[7]

Crown Ducal manufactured these plates commemorating the 1932 bicentennial of Washington's birth as part of a series illustrating important events in his life. The plates' image is based on the print by Thomas Barlow after the Rossiter and Mignot painting. The reverse of each plate reads: "George Washington Bicentennial Memorial Plates 1732-1932 / First in War, First in Peace, First in the Hearts of His Countrymen." Both the engraving and the plate are commercial ventures, yet both illustrate Rossiter's assertion that great men and their deeds inform and inspire the present.

Statuette of Lafayette at Yorktown by Jean Ossaye Mombur. David Bishop Skillman Library, Lafayette College.

Additional artifacts in Section III include:

Mort du General Lafayette
(The Death of General Layafette)
Unidentified artist, France
Hand-colored woodcut, 1834

Courtesy of David Bishop Skillman Library, Lafayette College
(MVLA, LC, N-YHS)

Lament for the Death of the Illustrious General La Fayette, June 25, 1834

Courtesy of David Bishop Skillman Library, Lafayette College
(MVLA, LC, N-YHS)

Order of Performance Commemorating the Death of the Marquis de Lafayette, September 6, 1834

Courtesy of David Bishop Skillman Library, Lafayette College
(MVLA, LC, N-YHS)

Eulogy on the Life and Character of La Fayette by Ashley Sampson, 1834

Courtesy of Tudor Place Historic House and Garden, Washington, D.C.
(MVLA)

Oration on the Life and Character of Gilbert Motier de Lafayette, 1835

The Gilder Lehrman Collection,
Courtesy of the Gilder Lehrman Institute of American History, NY
(MVLA, LC, N-YHS)

Ribbons
America
Silk, 1834

Courtesy of David Bishop Skillman Library, Lafayette College
(MVLA, LC, N-YHS)

Lafayette Dollars
Dies engraved by Charles E. Barber (1840-1917) and Paul Wayland Bartlett (1865-1925), both American
Silver, minted in 1899, inscribed "1900"

Courtesy of David Bishop Skillman Library, Lafayette College
(MVLA, LC, N-YHS)

MEDAL

America
White metal, 1835

Courtesy of David Bishop Skillman Library, Lafayette College
(MVLA, LC, N-YHS)

LAFAYETTE AT YORKTOWN

Jean Ossaye Mombur (1850-1896), French
Bronze, after 1875

Courtesy of David Bishop Skillman Library, Lafayette College
(MVLA, LC, N-YHS)

MEDAL

Peter L. Krider, American
Bronze, 1881

Courtesy of David Bishop Skillman Library, Lafayette College
(MVLA, LC, N-YHS)

MEDALS

M. Delannoy, French
Bronze, 1931

Courtesy of David Bishop Skillman Library, Lafayette College
(MVLA, LC, N-YHS)

MEDALS

Gaston-Albert Lavrillier (1885-1958), American
Bronze, 1932

Courtesy of David Bishop Skillman Library, Lafayette College
(MVLA, LC, N-YHS)

RIBBON

America
Silk, 1875

Courtesy of David Bishop Skillman Library, Lafayette College
(MVLA, LC, N-YHS)

GILBERT MOTIER MARQUIS DE LA FAYETTE

Edouard Gosselin, after Edme Quenedey (1756-1830), French
Aquatint, 1895

Courtesy of David Bishop Skillman Library, Lafayette College
(MVLA, LC, N-YHS)

Bibliography

ARTICLES

Reif, Rita. "Silent Witnesses to War and Fellowship," *The New York Times*, December 23, 2001.

Simpson, Robert and Carol. "Andrew Jackson's Historic Pistols, Part I," *The Gun Report* (January 1985), 16.

BOOKS AND PAMPHLETS

Abbot, W. W., and others, editors. *The Papers of George Washington, Colonial Series*, 10 volumes. Charlottesville: University Press of Virginia, 1983-1995.

Abbot, W. W., Dorothy Twohig, Philander D. Chase, and others, editors. *The Papers of George Washington, Revolutionary War Series*, 14 volumes to date. Charlottesville: University Press of Virginia, 1985-present.

Abbot, W. W., Dorothy Twohig, and others, editors. *The Papers of George Washington, Confederation Series*, 6 volumes. Charlottesville: University Press of Virginia, 1992-1997.

Abbot, W.W., Dorothy Twohig, Philander D. Chase, and others, editors. *The Papers of George Washington, Presidential Series*, 12 volumes to date. Charlottesville: University Press of Virginia, 1987-present.

Abbot, W. W., Dorothy Twohig, and others, editors. *The Papers of George Washington, Retirement Series*, 4 volumes. Charlottesville: University Press of Virginia, 1998-1999.

Adams, John Quincy. *Oration on the Life and Character of Gilbert Motier de Lafayette*. Washington: Gales and Seaton, 1835.

American Anti-Slavery Society. Garrison, William Lloyd, *Letter to Louis Kossuth, Concerning Freedom and Slavery in the United States*. Boston: R.F. Wallcut, 1852.

Baker, William Spohn. *Itinerary of George Washington From June 15, 1775, to December 23, 1783*. Philadelphia: J. B. Lippincott Company, 1892.

Bernier, Olivier. *Lafayette: Hero of Two Worlds*. New York: E. P. Dutton, Inc., 1983.

Biddle, Edward, and Mantle Fielding. *The Life & Works of Thomas Sully.* Philadelphia: Wickersham Press, 1921.

Billias, George Athan, editor. *George Washington's Generals.* New York: William Morrow and Company, 1964.

Boyd, Julian P., editor. *The Papers of Thomas Jefferson,* Volume 7. Princeton: Princeton University Press, 1953.

Brady, Patricia. *Martha Washington: An American Life.* New York: Viking, 2005.

Brandon, Edgar Ewing, compiler and editor. *A Pilgrimage of Liberty: A Contemporary Account of the Triumphal Tour of General Lafayette Through the Southern and Western States in 1825, as Reported by the Local Newspapers.* Athens: The Lawhead Press, 1944.

——————————————————————————. *Lafayette, Guest of the Nation: A Contemporary Account of the Triumphal Tour of General Lafayette Through the United States in 1824-1825 as Reported by the Local Newspapers,* 3 volumes. Oxford: The Oxford Historical Press, 1950-1957.

Brookhiser, Richard. *Founding Father: Rediscovering George Washington.* New York: The Free Press, 1996.

Congressional Record, July 24, 2002.

Ellis, Joseph J. *His Excellency George Washington.* New York: Alfred A. Knopf, 2004.

Fabian, Monroe H. *Mr. Sully, Portrait Painter: The Works of Thomas Sully (1783-1872),* reprint. Washington: UMI distributed by BCI, original publisher: Published for the National Portrait Gallery by the Smithsonian Institution, 1983.

Fitzpatrick, John C., editor. *The Writings of George Washington from the Original Manuscript Sources, 1745-1799,* 39 volumes. Washington: United States Government Printing Office, 1931-1944.

——————————————, editor. *The Last Will and Testament of George Washington and Schedule of his Property to which is appended the Last Will and Testament of Martha Washington,* 6th edition, revised. Mount Vernon, Virginia: Published through the generosity of Foley & Lardner by the Mount Vernon Ladies' Association of the Union, 1992.

Flexner, James Thomas. *Washington: The Indispensable Man.* New York: New American Library, 1984.

Gottschalk, Louis. *Lafayette Comes to America.* Chicago: The University of Chicago Press, 1935.

_____. *Lafayette Joins the American Army.* Chicago: The University of Chicago Press, 1937.

_____. *Lafayette and the Close of the American Revolution.* Chicago: The University of Chicago Press, 1942.

_____. *Lafayette Between the American & the French Revolution, 1783-1789.* Chicago: The University of Chicago Press, 1950.

_____. *The Letters of Lafayette to Washington, 1777-1799,* 2nd edition. Philadelphia: American Philosophical Society, 1976.

Higginbotham, Don. *George Washington and the American Military Tradition.* Athens: The University of Georgia Press, 1985.

Hume, Edgar Erskine. *Lafayette, the Virginia Mason,* reprinted from *The Virginia Masonic Herald,* Highland Springs, VA, Address delivered at Alexandria-Washington Lodge, No. 22, Alexandria, Virginia, May 24, 1934. The Society of the Cincinnati, Anderson House, Washington, D.C.

Idzerda, Stanley J., and others, editors. *Lafayette in the Age of the American Revolution: Selected Letters and Papers, 1776-1790,* 5 volumes. Ithaca: Cornell University Press, 1977-1983.

Idzerda, Stanley J., and others. *Lafayette, Hero of Two Worlds: The Art and Pageantry of His Farewell Tour of America, 1824-1825: Essays by Stanley J. Idzerda, Anne C. Loveland, and Marc H. Miller.* Flushing: Queens Museum, 1989.

Johnston, Elizabeth Bryant. *George Washington Day by Day.* New York: The Cycle Publishing Company, 1895.

Kramer, Lloyd. *Lafayette in Two Worlds: Public Cultures and Personal Identities in an Age of Revolutions.* Chapel Hill: The University of North Carolina Press, 1996.

Lafayette, General. *Memoirs Of General Lafayette With An Account Of His Visit To America And Of His Reception By The People Of The United States From His Arrival August 15th To The Celebration At Yorktown October 19th, 1824,* reprint. Whitefish, MT: Kessinger Publishing Company, 2004.

Lengel, Edward G. *George Washington: A Military Life.* New York: Random House, 2005.

Loveland, Anne C. *Emblem of Liberty: The Image of Lafayette in the American Mind.* Baton Rouge: Louisiana State University Press, 1971.

Malone, Dumas. *Jefferson and His Time,* Volume 2. Boston: Little, Brown and Co., 1951.

Maurois, Andre. *Adrienne: The Life of the Marquise de La Fayette,* translated from the French by Gerard Hopkins. London: Jonathan Cape, 1961.

Miller, Lillian B., and others, editors. *The Selected Papers of Charles Willson Peale and His Family, Charles Willson Peale: Artist in Revolutionary America, 1735-1791.* New Haven: Yale University Press for The National Portrait Gallery, Smithsonian Institution, 1983.

Mitnick, Barbara J., editor. *George Washington: American Symbol.* New York: Hudson Hills Press, in association with The Museums at Stony Brook and the Museum of Our National Heritage, 1999.

Nolan, James Bennett. *Lafayette in America, Day by Day.* Baltimore: The Johns Hopkins Press, 1934.

Poulet, Anne, and others. *Jean-Antoine Houdon: Sculptor of the Englightenment.* Washington: National Gallery of Art, in Association with the University of Chicago Press, Chicago and London, 2003.

Rossiter, T. P. *A Description of the Picture of the Home of Washington after the War.* New York: D. Appleton and Company, 1859.

Sears, Louis Martin. *George Washington & the French Revolution.* Detroit: Wayne State University Press, 1960.

Somkin, Fred. *Unquiet Eagle: Memory and Desire in the Idea of American Freedom, 1815-1860.* Ithaca: Cornell University Press, 1967.

Syrett, Harold C., and others, editors. *The Papers of Alexander Hamilton,* Volumes 15 and 24. New York: Columbia University Press, 1969 and 1976.

The New Encylopaedia Britannica, Micropaedia, fifteenth edition.

Unger, Harlow Giles. *Lafayette.* New York: J. Wiley & Sons, 2002.

MANUSCRIPTS

Library of Congress, Manuscript Division, Washington, D.C.
Microfilm, The Marquis de Lafayette Papers.

New York Public Library, Manuscript Division, in cooperation with Archives of American Art and Detroit Institute of Arts, New York, NY.

Microfilm, Thomas Sully, *Register of paintings executed by Thomas Sully between 1801-1871*.

Microfilm, Thomas Sully, *Journal of Thomas Sully's activities May 1792-1793, 1799-December 1846*.

Tudor Place Historic House and Garden, Washington, D.C.

Letter, George Washington Lafayette to George Washington Parke Custis, December 8, [1824].

Description of General La Fayette's Visit to Arlington House, no date.

WEBSITES

http://www.mountvernon.org

http://ww2.lafayette.edu/~library/special/marquis/marquis_home.htm

http://gwpapers.virginia.edu

http://memory.loc.gov/ammem/gwhtml/gwhome.html

http://friendsoflafayette.org/data/timeline.html

http://dlxs.library.cornell.edu/m/mayantislavery/

http://rmc.library.cornell.edu/FRENCHREV/Lafayette/exhibit/famimages/ifam_portrait_laf.htm

Mary V. Thompson
Research Specialist
The Mount Vernon Ladies' Association

Conclusion de la Campagne de 1781 en Virginie, *Noël Le Mire, after Jean-Baptiste Le Paon,*
ca. 1781. The Mount Vernon Ladies' Association.

George Washington
and the
Marquis de Lafayette:

A Chronology

(Key: Italics - Lafayette; Bold - George Washington and Lafayette)

1732

FEBRUARY 22

George Washington is born at Pope's Creek in Westmoreland County, Virginia. His father will die in 1743, when the boy is 11 years old.

1753-1758

George Washington serves as an official courier and later as a military officer in the French and Indian War, the struggle for control of the American frontier between England and France and their respective American Indian allies. At the end of this time, he resigns from the military and returns to Mount Vernon, his Virginia plantation.

1757

SEPTEMBER 6

Marie Joseph Paul Yves Roch Gilbert du Motier, Marquis de Lafayette is born at Château Chavaniac in southern France. Two years later, his father dies in a battle at Minden, Germany, fighting the British in the Seven Years' War (known in America as the French and Indian War).

1759-1775

Washington marries Martha Dandridge Custis, a young widow with two small children. He makes his living as a planter at Mount Vernon and begins serving in the Virginia House of Burgesses.

1769-1775

Washington becomes involved in the American colonies' struggle against Britain's attempt to tax them, without permitting them to be represented in Parliament.

1770-1771

Lafayette's inheritance makes him one of the wealthiest noblemen in Europe. He receives an appointment to serve in the King's Musketeers and begins his studies at the military academy at Versailles.

1774

Washington represents Virginia as a delegate to the First Continental Congress in Philadelphia.

Lafayette (age 16) marries Adrienne de Noailles (age 14).

1775

Washington serves as a delegate to the Second Continental Congress. While there, he is selected to lead the Continental Army and immediately goes to take command of the army at Cambridge, Massachusetts. He begins a siege of the city of Boston, which is occupied by the British.

While on military maneuvers, Lafayette meets the brother of the British king, George III, and learns about the colonial rebellion in America. He decides to volunteer to fight for the American cause.

1776

The British evacuate Boston, after a successful siege by American forces. The American colonies declare their independence from Britain. The next several months are marked by military defeats for American forces in New York and New Jersey. The year ends with a successful surprise attack by Washington on a Hessian garrison at Trenton, New Jersey, after a bold night-time crossing of the Delaware River.

In December, Lafayette signs a contract with Silas Deane, appointed by the Continental Congress to recruit foreign officers for the American cause. Lafayette accepts a commission as a major general in the American army.

1777

Early in the year, Washington is victorious against the British at the Battle of Princeton, New Jersey; he and the army go into winter quarters at Morristown, New Jersey.

FEBRUARY-JULY

Since Congress has no funds to bring him or other volunteers to America, Lafayette uses his own money to buy a ship, calling it the Victoire. *He secretly leaves for Bordeaux, where he makes plans to sail to America. The ship arrives in South Carolina in June, and the Marquis reaches Philadelphia in July.*

JULY 31

The Continental Congress gives Lafayette a commission as a major general in the Army of the United States. He meets Washington at a dinner in Philadelphia.

AUGUST 20

Lafayette arrives at Washington's camp, just north of Philadelphia.

SEPTEMBER

Washington and Lafayette are involved in a battle at Brandywine Creek in Pennsylvania, where Lafayette is shot in the leg.

OCTOBER

Washington attacks the British at Germantown, near Philadelphia, and is almost successful. Impressed by the American performance so soon after the defeat at Brandywine, the British retreat to Philadelphia for the winter, and France begins to look favorably on the Americans.

NOVEMBER

Lafayette joins Washington at his headquarters. He reconnoiters British positions outside of Philadelphia and is involved in a skirmish with the Hessians. Although outnumbered, Lafayette and his men win the day.

DECEMBER

At winter quarters in Valley Forge, Pennsylvania, Washington gives Lafayette command of one of the Virginia divisions in the Continental Army. During the winter, Washington sponsors Lafayette's induction into the American branch of the Masons (the young man was already a Mason in France). At this time, Washington's leadership of the Continental Army is threatened by some of his officers, a conspiracy known as the Conway Cabal.

1778

JANUARY-MARCH

Lafayette is given command of an expedition against Canada. He becomes involved in negotiations with the Iroquois, who agree to support the Americans.

FEBRUARY

A treaty of alliance and commerce is signed in Paris between France and the United States. England declares war on France.

APRIL

After Congress cancels the Canadian expedition, Lafayette returns to Valley Forge and resumes command of his Virginia division.

The Comte d'Estaing, with twelve ships of the line and four frigates, leaves France for America to fight the British.

MAY

Word reaches Valley Forge that the French have allied with the Americans. The American army celebrates with parades, sermons, musket and cannon fire, and an extra ration of rum for each soldier.

Lafayette's American Indian recruits (Oneida) arrive at Valley Forge. He sets out from camp with 2,200 men to scout the British in Philadelphia and becomes involved in a skirmish a few days later at Barren Hill. He manages to escape from 16,000 British troops under the command of Generals Howe, Grant, Clinton, and Grey.

JUNE

The British leave Philadelphia, headed for New York, by way of New Jersey. Washington makes General Benedict Arnold the military governor of the city.

Washington and Lafayette take part in the Battle of Monmouth in New Jersey; the Americans claim victory.

JULY

Word arrives that a French fleet, under the command of the Comte d'Estaing, and carrying an invasion force of 4,000 men, is in the Delaware Bay near Philadelphia. Washington sends Lafayette and 2,000 American soldiers north to assist the French in pushing the British out of New England.

AUGUST-SEPTEMBER

Lafayette and General Nathanael Greene visit the Comte d'Estaing on his ship. Lafayette is ordered to Rhode Island; he establishes his headquarters at Bristol.

OCTOBER

Lafayette spends three weeks in Philadelphia. On October 21, Congress grants him a temporary leave of absence to return to France.

DECEMBER

Lafayette bids farewell to Washington at Fishkill, New York.

1779

JANUARY-FEBRUARY

Washington is in winter quarters at Middlebrook, New Jersey.

Lafayette sails from Boston for France aboard the American ship, Alliance. *In France, he meets with officials, arguing for more aid for the Americans, who desperately need military supplies and troops.*

JULY

The American army captures the British garrison at Stony Point, New York.

Lafayette convinces the French foreign minister to send an expeditionary force to help the Americans and urges that French soldiers serve under Washington's command.

DECEMBER

Washington and the American army go into winter quarters at Morristown, New Jersey.

Lafayette's wife gives birth to a son who is christened George Washington, "as a tribute of respect and affection to my dear friend, General Washington."

At right, Ball Gown, silk satin and crepe, 1824. Courtesy of The Valentine Richmond History Center.

1780

JANUARY 25

Lafayette convinces Louis XVI and his ministers of the dangers of a British victory in the southern states.

FEBRUARY 29

Lafayette, in the uniform of an American major general, takes formal leave of the king and queen as he prepares to return to service with Washington.

MARCH-APRIL

Lafayette returns to America aboard the Hermione.

MAY

Lafayette reaches Washington's winter headquarters at Morristown, New Jersey, and relays Louis XVI's secret message that French expeditionary forces under the command of the Comte de Rochambeau will arrive with more than 6,000 men, artillery, munitions, ships, and money. Washington credits Lafayette with the help that will ensure American success. Louis XVI appoints Washington a lieutenant general in the French army and a vice admiral of its navy.

Congress passes a resolution honoring Lafayette for his gallantry and meritorious service.

JUNE

Lafayette, in the name of his wife, Adrienne, sends a sizeable contribution to Mrs. Joseph Reed in Philadelphia for her fundraising campaign to aid the American soldiers. Martha Washington, who is involved in the planning of the campaign, will donate $20,000 herself.

JULY

Washington sends Lafayette to Newport, Rhode Island, to confer with the Comte de Rochambeau and the Chevalier de Ternay, the admiral of the French fleet.

AUGUST

American General Horatio Gates is defeated by the British at Camden, South Carolina.

Washington gives Lafayette command of the Light Division, which is encamped on the west bank of the Hudson River, opposite New York.

SEPTEMBER

Lafayette accompanies George Washington, Alexander Hamilton, Henry Knox, several aides, and a cavalry escort, to Hartford, Connecticut, where they meet with Rochambeau. Washington and Lafayette leave for West Point, where they discover General Benedict Arnold's plot to turn the important American post over to the British.

Lafayette, along with General Knox, Lord Stirling, and eleven other generals, is appointed to decide the fate of Major John André, a British officer who conspired with Arnold and eventually was hanged.

NOVEMBER

Lafayette is named the first foreign member of the American Philosophical Society, an organization to which Washington also belongs.

DECEMBER

Washington goes into winter quarters at New Windsor, New York.

1781

JANUARY

Lafayette is with Washington at his winter quarters at New Windsor, New York. Troops from Pennsylvania and New Jersey mutiny over the issue of not being paid. While the Pennsylvania legislature makes financial concessions to their units, Washington orders all but one of the New Jersey mutineers to be executed.

FEBRUARY

General Nathanael Greene, who commands the southern theater of the war, asks Washington to send Lafayette to help stop the British general, Lord Cornwallis, in Virginia. Lafayette takes the Light Division to join Baron von Steuben in Virginia and strike at Benedict Arnold's forces, near Portsmouth. In the last days of the month, Lafayette is in Philadelphia to obtain additional men and supplies for the Virginia campaign.

MARCH

Lafayette's men leave Trenton, New Jersey, heading past Philadelphia for Wilmington, Delaware, and points south. Although Mrs. Washington is at her husband's winter quarters, Lafayette gives himself the "Pleasure of Seeing Mount Vernon" during a quick visit at the end of the month.

APRIL

Washington puts Lafayette in charge of military operations in Virginia, under the command of General Greene in the southern theater.

MAY

Lafayette orders the evacuation of Richmond, Virginia, which is about to be seized by Cornwallis.

JUNE

Lafayette and his men meet General Anthony Wayne on the Rappahannock River and learn of Washington's strategy for the next southern campaign.

Lafayette and his troops chase Cornwallis through Virginia. Cornwallis releases escaped slaves suffering from smallpox to spread the disease among the Americans and French.

Under the command of Washington and Rochambeau, combined American and French forces leave New York, heading south. They reach Philadelphia by the end of August.

SEPTEMBER

Lafayette, Wayne, and the French fleet under Admiral de Grasse bottle up Lord Cornwallis and his army at Yorktown, Virginia.

Washington and Rochambeau arrive at Williamsburg, Virginia, where they join Lafayette. At the end of the month, the combined French and American armies leave Williamsburg to begin the siege of Yorktown.

OCTOBER

Lafayette leads a charge against the British fortifications at Yorktown on the 14th. Three days later, Cornwallis proposes a cease-fire so that a surrender can be negotiated. The British formally surrender to the combined American and French armies on October 19th, ending the military phase of the war.

NOVEMBER

Lafayette leaves Yorktown at the beginning of the month, heading north to Philadelphia.

DECEMBER

George and Martha Washington arrive in Philadelphia, where they will spend the first part of the winter.

Late in the month, with the permission of Congress, Lafayette sets sail from Boston aboard the Alliance, *headed for France, where he will lobby his government for further aid to the United States.*

1782

JANUARY

Lafayette arrives in France. He is honored by the king and queen and promoted to maréchal de camp *(the equivalent to a major general or field marshall). He is one of the most celebrated men in Europe.*

MARCH

Washington returns to his headquarters at Newburgh, New York.

MAY

George Washington is approached by one of his officers about becoming king of the new United States, a suggestion he forcefully rejects.

SEPTEMBER

Lafayette's wife gives birth to the couple's fourth child, a daughter, who is called Virginie, in honor of Washington's home state of Virginia.

NOVEMBER

Britain and the United States sign a preliminary peace treaty, but it will not take effect until Britain and France also reach an agreement. Official word of the preliminary treaty will not reach America until March 1783.

1783

JANUARY

The British sign a treaty with America's allies, France and Spain, ending their conflict.

MARCH

Washington peacefully quells a threatened mutiny by officers in the Continental Army who have not received their pay. About ten days later, news of the treaty between Britain, France, and Spain arrives in the American camp.

APRIL

Congress ratifies the preliminary peace treaty of November 1782 and announces a cessation of hostilities.

MAY

In France, Lafayette is presented with the medal Le Chevalier de Saint James *for his service with the Continental Army.*

SEPTEMBER

The final peace treaty between Britain and the new United States is signed on September 3rd, ending the American Revolution. Word reaches Washington and the army at Princeton, New Jersey, sometime between October 30th and November 2nd.

NOVEMBER

British forces withdraw from New York City on November 25th.

DECEMBER

Washington bids farewell to his officers on December 4th in New York City. Later in the month, he resigns his military commission in Annapolis, Maryland. He immediately heads home to Mount Vernon, arriving on Christmas Eve.

1783-1799

Washington serves as President-General of the Society of the Cincinnati, a hereditary order of American and French officers, including Lafayette, who served in the American Revolution.

1784

Washington is active with canal projects to connect the frontier settlements in the Ohio Valley with ports on the Potomac River. He is made an honorary

The honour of M~i~s *Ann Morris*

company is requested at a FÊTE to be given to

GEN. LA FAYETTE, on ~~Friday~~ *monday* evening next,

1~0~th September, at the Castle Garden.

———◆———

Managers.

General Clarkson,	General Morton,
General Fish, *Genl Meredith*	General Mapes,
General Fleming,	Comm'y. Gen. Muir,
Col. Graham,	Col. Charles King,
Col. James I. Jones,	Hon. C. D. Colden,
A. Schermerhorn, Esq.	D. Lynch, Jr. Esq.

———

Committee.

Brig. Gen. Mount,	Brig. Gen. Paulding,
Col. Arcularius,	Col. Irving,
Col. Spicer,	Col. Tylee,
Col. Manly,	Col. Schieffelin,
Col. W. H. Maxwell,	Col. H. Maxwell,
Col. Chester,	Col. Nichols,
Major Geib,	Col. Purdy,
H. Brevoort, Esq.	Lieut. Col. Lee.

1824

member of the Library Society of Charleston, South Carolina, and is named chancellor of William and Mary College in Williamsburg, Virginia. Washington becomes a member of the board of visitors and governors of Washington College in Chestertown, Maryland, which was chartered in 1782 and named in his honor.

JUNE

Lafayette leaves Paris for America.

AUGUST

Lafayette arrives in New York in early August aboard the packet boat Courier de New York. **He is reunited with Washington on the 17th; the two spend the following week together at Mount Vernon with the Washington family and in Alexandria, Virginia.**

OCTOBER

Both Lafayette and his son, George Washington Lafayette, are named honorary citizens of Connecticut.

NOVEMBER

During the last two weeks of the month, Lafayette visits Washington at Richmond, Virginia, as well as at Mount Vernon and Annapolis, Maryland.

DECEMBER

Lafayette sets sail for France on the frigate Nymphe *on the 21st.*

1785-1789

Lafayette is elected to represent the nobility in the Estates General in Paris. He becomes a leader of the liberal aristocrats, advocating religious freedom and the abolition of the slave trade.

1785

Washington is president of the Potomac Company, seeking to improve transportation on that river. He hosts representatives from Maryland and Virginia at Mount Vernon to discuss issues relating to shared waterways. He also becomes a member of the Philadelphia Society for Promoting Agriculture and an honorary member of the South Carolina Society for Promoting Agriculture and Other Rural Concerns.

Adrienne de Lafayette sends presents from France to Martha Washington's four grandchildren. The marquis sends a family portrait of himself, his wife, and their three surviving children to Washington and later in the year, seven French hounds from the Comte and Comtesse d'Oilliamson.

At left, Invitation to a Fête for the Marquis de Lafayette at New York's Castle Garden, 1824. Courtesy of David Bishop Skillman Library, Lafayette College.

1787

Washington presides over the Constitutional Convention in Philadelphia; he signs the new Constitution.

Lafayette receives an honorary doctor of law degree from both Harvard and the University of Pennsylvania. He is named an honorary citizen of the states of Virginia, Maryland, and Massachusetts.

SEPTEMBER

Washington sends Lafayette a copy of the new United States Constitution.

1788

Washington encourages the states to ratify the Constitution. He also serves as master of the Masonic lodge in Alexandria, Virginia.

1789

Washington is unanimously elected first President of the United States and travels to New York for his inauguration on April 30th. He makes a tour of New England states and becomes an honorary member of the Holland Masonic Lodge in New York City.

MAY

Lafayette supports efforts to convert the Estates General into a revolutionary National Assembly. He sets out to reform the justice system in France.

JULY

At the National Assembly in Paris on the 11th, Lafayette introduces his version of the Declaration of the Rights of Man and of Citizens. He is elected Vice President of the National Assembly two days later. The French Revolution begins on July 14th with the storming of the Bastille, a large prison where political opponents of the government were incarcerated.

OCTOBER

Lafayette's troops save King Louis XVI and Queen Marie Antoinette from a crowd which has stormed the palace at Versailles. He escorts the royal couple to Paris where they become hostages.

1789-1790

Lafayette supports actions to transfer power from the aristocracy to the bourgeoisie.

1790

Washington makes a tour of Long Island and receives an honorary doctorate from Brown University.

Lafayette receives an honorary doctor of laws degree from Princeton University.

Lafayette sends the key to the main door of the Bastille to President Washington.

1791

DECEMBER

Washington makes a tour of the Southern states.

Lafayette is appointed commander of the French army at Metz to counter an Austrian invasion of France. He hopes to suppress radicals who are trying to take over the direction of the French Revolution.

1792

APRIL

France declares war on Austria.

AUGUST

The French monarchy is overthrown on August 10th. Radical revolutionaries demand the arrest of Lafayette and all other aristocrats, planning to prosecute them for treason and execute them. Lafayette flees to Belgium on August 19th, but is turned over to the Austrians and held prisoner. He argues that he should be released because of his American citizenship.

Washington is made an honorary citizen of France by a decree of the French National Assembly on August 26th.

SEPTEMBER

Adrienne, the Marquise de Lafayette, is arrested at Château Chavaniac and confined there.

1793

Washington again is unanimously elected to serve a second term as President of the United States.

The Reign of Terror, a period in which radicals take control of the government, begins in France. More than 1,000 people, mostly aristocrats, are guillotined.

1794

Lafayette is in Olmütz Prison. His wife, Adrienne, is transferred to a Paris prison with her grandmother, mother, and sister. All are condemned to the guillotine; Adrienne's three relatives are executed.

In January, Washington writes to the King of Prussia, asking for a personal favor—the release of Lafayette from prison. Later in the year, the United States government sends to Europe an amount of money equal to the salary Lafayette refused to take during the Revolution, in order to help him during his imprisonment.

The Whiskey Rebellion, a revolt against paying taxes on spirits to the federal government, breaks out in western Pennsylvania; Washington leads troops to the area.

1795

JANUARY

Adrienne de Lafayette is freed from prison in Paris, after prominent Americans pressure French officials.

APRIL-OCTOBER

Fifteen-year-old George Washington Lafayette is sent by his mother to America until the political situation improves in France. Adrienne de Lafayette asks the Austrian government to allow her and her daughters, Anastasie and Virginie, to join the marquis. The women are permitted to join him in his cell at Olmütz on October 24th.

NOVEMBER

A new government, known as La Directoire, *begins in France.*

1796

George Washington Lafayette goes to the executive mansion in Philadelphia in April to meet his namesake. As a member of the household, he develops a close relationship with the Washington family over the next eighteen months.

Washington declines a third term as president. He issues his Farewell Address, which is widely published, in September.

Gouverneur Morris, representing the state of New York, arrives in Vienna in September to negotiate the release of Lafayette.

1797

Washington retires as president in March and leaves Philadelphia for Mount Vernon. George Washington Lafayette remains with the family as a beloved guest.

In September, Lafayette, his wife, and daughters are liberated from prison in Austria thanks to American assistance.

George Washington Lafayette leaves Mount Vernon in October.

1798

George Washington Lafayette returns to Europe; the family is reunited in Denmark in February.

When war threatens with France, President John Adams names Washington commander in chief of the armies of the United States of America. The war never breaks out.

1799

Turmoil continues in France. Napoleon comes to power and unsuccessfully prohibits Lafayette from entering the country because of his liberal democratic ideas. Lafayette takes up life as a gentleman farmer at La Grange.

DECEMBER 14

Washington dies at age 67 at Mount Vernon of a severe throat infection; his body is placed in the old family vault at Mount Vernon.

1802

Washington's widow, Martha Dandridge Custis Washington, dies a few weeks before her 70th birthday.

1807

Adrienne, the Marquise de Lafayette, dies at the age of 47.

1815-1824

Lafayette serves several terms in the Chamber of Deputies and is a strong supporter of liberal policies and the common people.

1824

JANUARY

Congressman George E. Mitchell of Maryland submits a joint resolution inviting Lafayette to visit the United States. It is passed by both houses of Congress.

AUGUST

Lafayette arrives in New York, with an invitation from President James Monroe, aboard the packet boat Cadmus *with his son, George Washington Lafayette, and his secretary, Auguste Levasseur. The thirteen-month visit engenders great interest throughout the country, and celebrations, parades, triumphal arches, dinners, and balls ensue. He travels first to Massachusetts.*

SEPTEMBER

Lafayette visits New Hampshire, Massachusetts, Connecticut and New York.

SEPTEMBER 28-OCTOBER 6

Lafayette travels in New Jersey and Pennsylvania, on the way to Philadelphia, where he gives an impressive speech at the State House (now known as Independence Hall).

OCTOBER

The Marquis visits Pennsylvania, Delaware, Maryland, the District of Columbia, and Virginia.

Lafayette sails down the Potomac on the 17th, on the way to Yorktown, accompanied by Martha Washington's grandson, George Washington Parke Custis, and "a large crowd of notables." Lafayette arrives at Mount Vernon, while a salute is fired from across the river at Fort Washington. He spends an entire hour alone at Washington's tomb.

NOVEMBER

Lafayette is in Virginia, the District of Columbia, and Maryland. During this month, he visits Thomas Jefferson at Monticello and James Madison at Montpelier.

DECEMBER

Lafayette spends the month in the District of Columbia, Maryland, and Virginia. He gives an address to both houses of Congress, the first foreign dignitary to do so. He also gives a speech under the Liberty Tree in Annapolis, Maryland.

Lafayette visits Martha Washington's youngest granddaughter, Nelly Custis Lewis, and her family at Woodlawn Plantation, near Mount Vernon.

1825

JANUARY

The marquis travels between the District of Columbia, Maryland, and Virginia. He goes to Arlington House for several days to visit George Washington Parke Custis. He receives an honorary degree from the Columbian Institute of Washington. At the end of the month, he travels to Pennsylvania.

FEBRUARY

Lafayette is in Pennsylvania, Maryland, and the District of Columbia. He attends a meeting of the Colonization Society and a Masonic dinner in Washington. Towards the end of the month, he begins a southern tour, traveling to Virginia and North Carolina.

MARCH

Lafayette visits North and South Carolina, Georgia, the Creek Reservation, and Alabama.

APRIL

The marquis tours Alabama, then sails to New Orleans and proceeds by boat up the Mississippi River, where he makes stops in Natchez, Mississippi, St. Louis, Missouri, and Kaskeskia, Illinois.

MAY

Lafayette goes by steamboat back down the Mississippi, to the Ohio River, ascends the Cumberland River, and reaches Tennessee before continuing on to Kentucky, Ohio, present-day West Virginia, and Pennsylvania.

JUNE

Lafayette travels through western Pennsylvania and New York, visiting Niagara Falls, before reaching Boston to celebrate the fifty-year anniversary of the Battle of Bunker Hill. Later in the month, he tours New England, passing through New Hampshire, Maine, and Vermont.

JULY

Lafayette is in New York, before going on to New Jersey, Pennsylvania, and Maryland. During the month, he visits Revolutionary War battlefields and is made an honorary member of the Philadelphia Athenaeum.

Lafayette is in Maryland, the District of Columbia, and Virginia. He pays visits to newly-retired President James Monroe, James and Dolley Madison, and Thomas Jefferson. Lafayette again travels to Woodlawn Plantation to see Nelly Custis Lewis, who presents to him one of the needlework chair cushions made by her grandmother, Martha Washington.

SEPTEMBER

On the 7th, Lafayette leaves the District of Columbia on the steamship Mount Vernon. *Two days later, he sails for France on the American frigate* Brandywine, *having visited each of the twenty-four states then in the Union.*

1826

Lafayette College is founded to honor the marquis.

1830

Lafayette supports the Polish Revolution with speeches in the Chamber of Deputies, financial donations, entertaining of exiled politicians, and as a founding member of the Polish Committee.

JULY

Lafayette commands the National Guard which assists in overthrowing King Charles X and putting Louis Philippe on the French throne.

1831

Washington's body is moved from the old family vault at Mount Vernon to the New Tomb.

Lafayette begins a national campaign to encourage the French government to support Poland and take actions against Russian despotism. He has the support of fifty French politicians, journalists, and writers.

1832

For the centennial celebration of Washington's birth, sculptor Horatio Greenough is commissioned to create a statue of Washington for the rotunda of the United States Capitol (now at the Smithsonian Institution).

1834

MAY 20

Lafayette dies in Paris, just four months before his 77th birthday. He is buried three days later in that city's Picpus Cemetery, next to his wife. George Washington Lafayette scatters around the coffin American soil that Lafayette brought back for his grave. America mourns the loss, and both houses of the Unites States Congress are draped in black.

1917

During World War I, Americans came to the aid of France. On July 4, 1917, as a way of acknowledging that the United States was repaying its debt for French assistance during the American Revolution, American Lieutenant Colonel Charles E. Stanton uttered the phrase, "Lafayette, we are here!" at Lafayette's tomb.

1976

President Gerald Ford posthumously promotes George Washington to the rank of six-star General of the Armies.

2002

Virginia Senator John Warner sponsors a bill, passed in the United States Senate, making Lafayette an honorary citizen. Only five people before him have received a similar honor.

Mary V. Thompson
Research Specialist
The Mount Vernon Ladies' Association

NOTES TO INTRODUCTORY ESSAY

1   Lafayette to Washington, 17 March 1790, in *The Papers of George Washington: Presidential Series,* Abbot and others, 5:242; Thomas Paine to Washington, 1 May 1790 (ibid., 5:369). Full citations of sources provided in the bibliography at the end of this catalog. Quotations throughout this essay reproduce capitalizations and spellings of the original manuscripts. The author wishes to acknowledge Barton C. Shaw for his seasoned "advices" on writing history and Paul Schlueter for his keen-eyed copy editing.

2   Washington to Gouverneur Morris, 24 July 1778, in *Lafayette in the Age of the American Revolution,* Idzerda and others, 2:116-117.

3   Biographical details on Lafayette are taken from the following sources: Idzerda and others, *Lafayette in the Age of the American Revolution;* Gottschalk, *The Letters of Lafayette to Washington, 1777-1799,* 2nd ed.; Gottschalk, *Lafayette Comes to America;* Gottschalk, *Lafayette Joins the American Army;* Gottschalk, *Lafayette and the Close of the American Revolution;* Gottschalk, *Lafayette between the American and French Revolution;* Howard H. Peckham, "Marquis de Lafayette: Eager Warrior," in *George Washington's Generals,* Billias, 212-238; and Unger, *Lafayette.*

4   In his memoir of 1779, Lafayette wrote that he "dared to take for a device on my coat-of-arms the words *Cur Non?,* which could serve me both as an encouragement and as a response." The motto had also been that of his ancestor, the Maréchal de Lafayette (ca. 1380-1462). Idzerda and others, *Lafayette in the Age of the American Revolution,* 1:7, 13n; Lafayette to Adrienne de Noailles de Lafayette, 7 June 1777 (ibid., 1:58-59).

5   Memoir by the Chevalier Dubuysson, ibid., 1:76-77; Resolution of Congress, 31 July 1777 (ibid., 1:88).

6   Ibid., 1:86n, 88n.

7   Lafayette's memoir of 1779, ibid., 1:91.

8   Ibid.

9   Washington to Benjamin Harrison, 19 August, 1777, ibid., 1:104.

10 Lafayette to Washington, 14 October 1777, ibid., 1:122.

11 Ellis, *His Excellency,* 116.

12 Idzerda and others, *Lafayette in the Age of the American Revolution,* 1:168.

13 Kramer, *Lafayette in Two Worlds,* 21-22.

14 Lafayette to Washington, 14 October 1777, in *Lafayette in the Age of the American Revolution,* Idzerda and others, 1:123; Lafayette to the Duc d'Ayen, 16 December 1777 (ibid., 1:194).

15 Letter accompanying the memoir by the Chevalier Dubuysson, 12 September [1777], ibid., 1:84.

16 Idzerda and others, *Lafayette in the Age of the American Revolution,* 1:101n.

17 Lafayette to Adrienne de Noailles de Lafayette, 1 October 1777, ibid., 1:116; Washington to the President of Congress, 1 November 1777 (ibid., 1:140-141).

18 Greene quoted in letter of Washington to the President of Congress, 26 November 1777, ibid., 1:159.

19 Historians have debated the seriousness of the "Conway Cabal," a plot to replace Washington with Horatio Gates as commander in chief of the Continental Army, but Lafayette certainly believed the threat was real. Lafayette to the Duc d'Ayen, 16 December 1777, ibid., 1:192; Lafayette to Henry Laurens [ca. 5 January 1777] (ibid., 1:216); Lafayette to Washington, 30 December 1777 (ibid., 1:206); Lafayette's memoir of 1779 (ibid., 1:172).

20 Lafayette to Washington, 19 February 1778, ibid., 1:299-301; Washington to Lafayette, 10 March 1778 (ibid., 1:342-343).

21 Washington to Gouverneur Morris, 29 May 1778, in *The Writings of George Washington,* Fitzpatrick, 11:485.

22 Lafayette's memoir of 1779, in *Lafayette in the Age of the American Revolution*, Idzerda and others, 2:11.

23 Washington to Lafayette, 1 September 1778, ibid., 2:166.

24 Lafayette's memoir of 1779, ibid., 2:18; Washington to Lafayette, 30 September 1779 (ibid., 1:314).

25 Lafayette's "Observations on Matters Pertaining to the Navy for an Expedition to North America," 21 February 1780, ibid., 2:357. In this document Lafayette goes on to say: "We must show more respect to the uniform of an American general officer and to the dignity of a state governor than we might show in a similar case to Prussians and emperors. The Americans are very responsive to these signs of regard." (ibid.).

26 George Washington to the President of Congress, 13 May 1780, ibid., 3:11.

27 Lafayette to Washington, 14 August 1780, ibid., 3:142; Washington to Lafayette, 30 October 1780 (ibid., 3: 214).

28 Lafayette had been with Washington at West Point when Arnold's treason was discovered in September 1780, and he participated in the court-martial that resulted in the hanging of the British spy Major John André.

29 Lafayette to Washington, 23 April 1781, in *Lafayette in the Age of the American Revolution*, Idzerda and others, 4:60; Washington to Lafayette, 4 May 1781 (ibid., 4:84, 85n).

30 Lafayette to Washington, 24 May 1781, ibid., 4:131; Lafayette to the Vicomte de Noailles, 9 July 1781 (ibid., 4:241).

31 Washington to Lafayette, 2 September 1781, ibid., 4:385.

32 Reported by St. George Tucker to his wife, ibid., 4:397n.

33 Lafayette to the Comte de Maurepas, 20 October 1781, ibid., 4:422.

34 Lafayette to Washington, 21 December 1781, ibid., 4:450.

35 Lafayette to Washington, 5 February 1783, ibid., 5:90-92; Washington to Lafayette, 5 April, 1783 (ibid., 5:121).

36 Lafayette to Washington, 8 September 1783, ibid., 5:153; Lafayette to Washington, 9 March 1784 (ibid., 209); Ellis, *His Excellency*, 158-59 discusses Washington and the "heredity clause."

37 Lafayette to Adrienne de Noailles de Lafayette, 20 August 1784, in *Lafayette in the Age of the American Revolution,* Idzerda and others, 5:237.

38 Washington to Adrienne de Noailles de Lafayette, 25 November 1784, in *The Papers of George Washington: Confederation Series,* Abbot and others, 2:150.

39 Washington to Lafayette, 8 December 1784, in *Lafayette in the Age of the American Revolution*, Idzerda and others, 5:279; Lafayette to Washington, 21 December 1784, in *The Papers of George Washington: Confederation Series,* Abbot and others, 2:226-228.

40 Washington to Lafayette, 25 July 1785, in *Lafayette in the Age of the American Revolution,* Idzerda and others, 5:339.

41 Lafayette to Washington, 6 February, 1786, in *The Papers of George Washington: Confederation Series*, Abbot and others, 3:544.

42 Washington to Lafayette, 10 May 1786, ibid., 4:43.

43 Lafayette to Washington, 3 August 1787, ibid., 5:281.

44 Washington to Lafayette, 18 September 1787, ibid., 5:334.

45 Lafayette to Washington, 1 January 178[8], ibid., 6:5.

46 Washington to Lafayette, 28 April 1788, ibid., 6:245.

47 Washington to Thomas Jefferson, 13 March 1793, in *The Papers of George Washington: Presidential Series,* Abbot and others, 12:313.

48 Washington to Alexander Hamilton, 22 December 1795, in *The Writings of George Washington,* Fitzpatrick, 34:404.

49 Washington to Lafayette, 8 October 179[7], in *The Papers of George Washington: Retirement Series,* Abbot and others, 1:391.

50 Washington's will, 9 July 1799, in *The Last Will and Testament of George Washington,* Fitzpatrick, 2.

51 Quoted in William Lloyd Garrison, *Letter to Louis Kossuth, Concerning Freedom and Slavery in the United States*, 39-40. On-line resource in the Samuel J. May Anti-Slavery Collection, Division of Rare and Manuscript Collections, Cornell University Library: http://dlxs.library.cornell.edu/m/mayantislavery/.

52 Levasseur quoted in Brandon, *Lafayette, Guest of the Nation,* 42-43.

NOTES TO SECTION I

1 Lafayette, *Memoir of 1779*, in *Lafayette in the Age of the American Revolution: Selected Letters and Papers*, 1776-1790, eds. Idzerda and others (Ithaca: Cornell University Press, 1977), 1:7. (Hereafter cited as *Lafayette: Selected Letters.*)

2 Lafayette to Adrienne de Noailles de Lafayette, 6 January [1778], *Lafayette: Selected Letters*, 1:223.

3 Washington to Franklin, 28 December 1778, *The Writings of George Washington from the Original Manuscript Sources*, 1745-1799, ed. Fitzpatrick (Washington: United States Government Printing Office, 1936), 13:459. (Hereafter cited as *Writings.*)

4 Washington to Huntington, 13 May 1780, *Writings*, 18:351-352.

5 Lafayette to Washington, 8 July 1781, *Lafayette: Selected Letters*, 4:239.

6 Lafayette to Samuel Cooper, 26 October, 1781, *Lafayette: Selected Letters*, 4:429, 431. According to a note in this source, Cooper was an ardent propagandist for the French alliance; Lafayette thus knew his news would reach the widest possible audience.

7 For further discussion of this topic, please see the catalog entries regarding Lafayette and Washington letters of 5 February 1783 and 5 April 1783.

8 Lafayette to Washington, 30 March 1782, *Lafayette: Selected Letters*, 5:22.

9 Washington to Lafayette, 5 April 1783, *Lafayette: Selected Letters*, 5:120.

10 As reported in the *Portsmouth Journal,* November 20, 1824. Cited in Malone, *Jefferson and His Time* (Boston: Little, Brown and Co., 1951), 2:46.

11 Washington to Lafayette, 10 October 1783, *Writings*, 27:215-218.

12 Washington to Anastasie de Lafayette, 25 November 1784, *The Papers of George Washington: Confederation Series*, eds. Abbot, Twohig, and others (Charlottesville: University Press of Virginia, 1992), 2:150. (Hereafter cited as *Papers of Washington, Confederation Series.*)

13 Lafayette to Washington, 1 January 178[8], *Papers of Washington, Confederation Series*, 6:5.

14 Lafayette to Adrienne de Noailles de Lafayette, 20 August 1784, *Lafayette: Selected Letters*, 5:237.

15 Madison to Jefferson, 7 September 1784, *The Papers of Thomas Jefferson*, ed. Boyd (Princeton, New Jersey: Princeton University Press, 1953), 7:416.

16 Lafayette to Jefferson, 11 October 1784, ibid., 7:438.

17 *The New Encyclopaedia Britannica, Micropaedia*, fifteenth edition, s.v. "Rights of Man and of the Citizen, Declaration of the," 10:71.

18 Washington to the King of Prussia, 15 January 1794, *The Papers of Alexander Hamilton*, eds. Syrett and others (New York: Columbia University Press, 1969), 15:638n.

19 Washington to Lafayette, 8 October 179[7], *The Papers of George Washington, Retirement Series,* eds. Twohig and others (Charlottesville: University Press of Virginia, 1998), 1:390.

20 Lafayette to Alexander Hamilton, 7 March 1800, *Papers of Alexander Hamilton,* eds. Syrett and others (New York: Columbia University Press, 1976), 24:297-298, 298n.

21 Martha Washington to Lafayette, 31 October 1800, The Marquis de Lafayette Papers, Manuscript Division, Library of Congress, Washington, D.C. Reel 25, folder 258.

22 Anne Poulet and others, *Jean-Antoine Houdon: Sculptor of the Enlightenment* (Washington, DC: National Gallery of Art, in Association with the University of Chicago Press, Chicago and London, 2003), 20.

23 Ibid., 260, 262n.

24 Robert and Carol Simpson, "Andrew Jackson's Historic Pistols, Part I," *The Gun Report* (January 1985): 16.

25 Rita Reif, "Silent Witnesses to War and Fellowship," *The New York Times,* December 23, 2001.

26 Washington to Charles Willson Peale, 12 December 1780, *Writings* 20:463.

27 Charles Willson Peale to Martha Washington, 16 January 1781, *The Selected Papers of Charles Willson Peale and His Family, Charles Willson Peale: Artist in Revolutionary America, 1735-1791,* eds. Miller and others (New Haven and London: Yale University Press for The National Portrait Gallery, Smithsonian Institution, 1983), 360.

28 Lafayette to Washington, 30 March 1782, *Lafayette: Selected Papers,* 5:22. (Text cited follows editor's convention: words written in cipher by Lafayette and deciphered between the lines by Washington are shown in capitals.)

29 "Recommendation for James," Lafayette, 21 November 1784, *Lafayette: Selected Papers,* 5:277, 279.

30 Lafayette to Washington, 5 February 1783, *Lafayette: Selected Papers.,* 5:91-92.

31 Lafayette to Washington, 17 March 1790, *The Papers of George Washington, Presidential Series,* eds. Twohig and others (Charlottesville: University Press of Virginia, 1996), 5:242. (Hereafter cited as *Papers of Washington, Presidential Series.)*

32 Ibid.

33 Washington to Lafayette, 11 August 1790, *Papers of Washington, Presidential Series,* 6:233.

34 Ibid.

35 George Washington to Bushrod Washington, 22 September 1783, *Writings,* 27:161.

36 Washington to Lafayette, 30 October 1783, *Writings,* 27:215.

37 Ibid.

38 Washington to Charles Willson Peale, 9 January 1787, *Papers of Washington, Confederation Series,* 4:506.

NOTES TO SECTION II

1   General Lafayette, *Memoirs Of General Lafayette With An Account Of His Visit To America And Of His Reception By The People Of The United States From His Arrival August 15th To The Celebration At Yorktown October 19th, 1824* (repr., Whitefish, MT: Kessinger Publishing Company, 2004), 68.

2   Edgar Ewing Brandon, ed., *Lafayette, Guest of the Nation: A Contemporary Account of the Triumphal Tour of General Lafayette Through the United States in 1824-1825 as Reported by the Local Newspapers* (Oxford, Ohio: The Oxford Historical Press, 1950), 1:38.

3   General Lafayette, *Memoirs Of General Lafayette With An Account Of His Visit To America And Of His Reception By The People Of The United States From His Arrival August 15th To The Celebration At Yorktown October 19th, 1824* (repr., Whitefish, MT: Kessinger Publishing Company, 2004, 67.

4   Anne C. Loveland, "Lafayette's Farewell Tour," *Lafayette, Hero of Two Worlds: The Art and Pageantry of His Farewell Tour of America, 1824-1825* (Hanover and London: The Queens Museum, University Press of New England, 1989), 70-71.

5   Edgar Erskine Hume, *Lafayette, the Virginia Mason,* reprinted from *The Virginia Masonic Herald,* Highland Springs, VA, Address delivered at Alexandria-Washington Lodge, No. 22, Alexandria, Virginia, May 24, 1934. The Society of the Cincinnati, Anderson House, Washington, D.C.

6   George Washington Lafayette to George Washington Parke Custis, 8 December [1824], Tudor Place Historic House and Garden, Washington, D.C.

7   Description of General La Fayette's Visit to Arlington House, undated, Tudor Place Historic House and Garden, Washington, D.C.

8   Thomas Sully, *Register of paintings executed by Thomas Sully between 1801-1871* (New York: microfilm made by New York Public Library Manuscript Division in cooperation with Archives of American Art and Detroit Institute of Arts, 1956), p. 47, N18.

9   Thomas Sully, *Journal of Thomas Sully's activities May 1792-1793, 1799-December 1846* (New York: microfilm made by New York Public Library Manuscript Division in cooperation with Archives of American Art and Detroit Institute of Arts, 1956), p. 32, N18.

10   Edward Biddle and Mantle Fielding, *The Life & Works of Thomas Sully* (Philadelphia: Wickersham Press, 1921), 36.

11   Monroe H. Fabian, *Mr. Sully, Portrait Painter: The Works of Thomas Sully (1783-1872),* (repr. Washington: UMI distributed by BCI, original publisher: Published for the National Portrait Gallery by the Smithsonian Institution, c1983), ill. 37.

12   Thomas Sully, *Register of paintings executed by Thomas Sully between 1801-1871* (New York: microfilm made by New York Public Library Manuscript Division in cooperation with Archives of American Art and Detroit Institute of Arts, 1956), pp. 50, 51, 53, 56, 59, 62, 64, 66, 69, N18.

13　Lafayette to Washington, 18 April 1781, *Lafayette In the Age of the American Revolution: Selected Letters & Papers, 1776-1790,* eds. Idzerda and others (Ithaca: Cornell University, 1981), 4:43, 45.

14　Edgar Ewing Brandon, ed., *Lafayette, Guest of the Nation: A Contemporary Account of the Triumphal Tour of General Lafayette Through the United States in 1824-1825 as Reported by the Local Newspapers* (Oxford, Ohio: The Oxford Historical Press, 1950), 1:37.

15　Edgar Erskine Hume, *Lafayette, the Virginia Mason,* reprinted from *The Virginia Masonic Herald,* Highland Springs, VA, Address delivered at Alexandria-Washington Lodge, No. 22, Alexandria, Virginia, May 24, 1934. The Society of the Cincinnati, Anderson House, Washington, D.C.

16　*National Journal of Washington,* September 10, 1825. Cited in J. Bennett Nolan, *Lafayette in America Day by Day* (Baltimore: The Johns Hopkins Press, 1934), 306.

NOTES TO SECTION III

1　John Quincy Adams, *Oration on the Life and Character of Gilbert Motier de Lafayette* (Washington, D.C.: Gales and Seaton, 1835), 35.

2　Franklin Delano Roosevelt, quoted in the *New York Times,* May 21, 1934, 1. Cited in Anne C. Loveland, *Emblem of Liberty: The Image of Lafayette in the American Mind* (Baton Rouge: Louisiana State University Press, 1971), 146.

3　Senator John Warner, quoted in the *Congressional Record,* July 24, 2002 (Senate), S7302-S7303.

4　Edgar Ewing Brandon, ed., *Lafayette, Guest of the Nation: A Contemporary Account of the Triumphal Tour of General Lafayette Through the United States in 1824-1825 as Reported by the Local Newspapers* (Oxford, Ohio: The Oxford Historical Press, 1957), 3:65. We thank Jean B. Lee, Professor of History at the University of Wisconsin – Madison, for sharing this information with us.

5　Michael J. McAfee, Curator of History at the West Point Museum, kindly identified uniforms in this print.

6　T. P. Rossiter, *A Description of the Picture of the Home of Washington after the War* (New York: D. Appleton and Company, 1859), 9.

7　Lafayette to Adrienne de Noailles de Lafayette, 20 August 1784, *Lafayette in the Age of the American Revolution: Selected Letters and Papers, 1776-1790,* eds. Idzerda and others (Ithaca: Cornell University Press, 1983), 5:237.

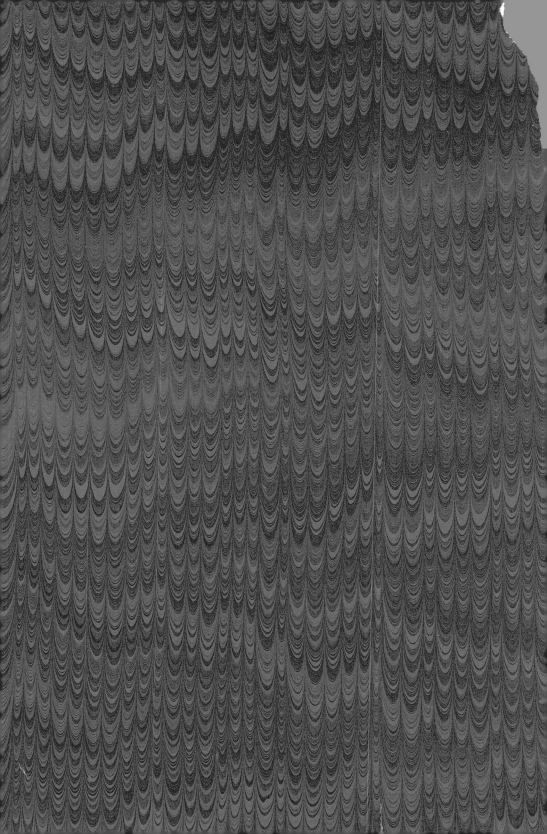